Holt
Mathematics

Course 2
Homework and Practice
Workbook

HOLT, RINEHART AND WINSTON

A Harcourt Education Company

Orlando • **Austin** • New York • San Diego • London

ISBN 0-03-078321-6

4 5   170   09 08 07

CONTENTS

Holt Mathematics

CONTENTS, *CONTINUED*

Holt Mathematics

CONTENTS, *CONTINUED*

Holt Mathematics

CONTENTS, *CONTINUED*

Holt Mathematics

Practice
LESSON 1-1   *Numbers and Patterns*

Identify a possible pattern. Use the pattern to write the next three numbers.

1. 41, 37, 33, 29, ____, ____, ____, ...

_____

_____

2. 50, 52, 56, 62, ____, ____, ____, ...

_____

_____

3. 320, 160, 80, 40, ____, ____, ____, ...

_____

_____

4. 24, 40, 56, 72, ____, ____, ____, ...

_____

_____

Identify a possible pattern. Use the pattern to draw the next three figures.

5. △ ○ □ ○ □ ○ △ ○ ○ □ ○ △

_____

6.

_____

7. Complete the table so that it shows the number of dots in each figure.

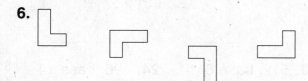

Figure 1   Figure 2   Figure 3   Figure 4   Figure 5

Figure	1	2	3
Number of Dots			

How many dots are in the fifth figure of the pattern? ____

Use drawings to justify your answer.

Holt Mathematics

Practice
LESSON 1-2
Exponents

Find each value.

1. 5^2 **2.** 2^4 **3.** 3^3 **4.** 7^2

_____   _____   _____   _____

5. 4^4 **6.** 12^2 **7.** 10^3 **8.** 11^1

_____   _____   _____   _____

9. 1^6 **10.** 20^2 **11.** 6^3 **12.** 7^3

_____   _____   _____   _____

Write each number using an exponent and the given base.

13. 16, base 4   **14.** 25, base 25   **15.** 100, base 10   **16.** 125, base 5

_____   _____   _____   _____

17. 32, base 2   **18.** 243, base 3   **19.** 900, base 30   **20.** 121, base 11

_____   _____   _____   _____

21. 3,600, base 60   **22.** 256, base 4   **23.** 512, base 8   **24.** 196, base 14

_____   _____   _____   _____

25. Damon has 4 times as many stamps as Julia. Julia has 4 times as many stamps as Claire. Claire has 4 stamps. Write the number of stamps Damon has in both exponential form and standard form.

_____

26. Holly starts a jump rope exercise program. She jumps rope for 3 minutes the first week. In the second week, she triples the time she jumps. In the third week, she triples the time of the second week, and in the fourth week, she triples the time of the third week. How many minutes does she jump rope during the fourth week?

_____

Holt Mathematics

Practice

LESSON 1-3

Metric Measurements

Choose the most appropriate metric unit for each measurement. Justify your answer.

1. The capacity of a paper cup

_____

_____

_____

_____

2. The mass of a small poodle.

_____

_____

_____

_____

3. The width of a computer screen

_____

_____

_____

_____

4. The mass of a pencil

_____

_____

_____

_____

Convert each measure.

5. 496 mm to centimeters

_____

6. 0.68 kg to grams

_____

7. 3,800 mL to liters

_____

8. 832 mg to grams

_____

9. 76 km to meters

_____

10. 2.9 cm to meters

_____

11. 0.041kL to liters

_____

12. 14.9 g to milligrams

_____

13. 7,800 cm to meters

_____

14. Sam's laptop computer has a mass of 4.2 kg. Fred's laptop computer has a mass of 4,940 grams. Which computer has the lesser mass? Explain your answer.

_____

15. Elise makes a poster that is 1.5 m tall. Meg makes a poster that is 96 cm tall. Who makes a taller poster? Explain your answer.

_____

Holt Mathematics

LESSON
1-4
Practice
Applying Exponents

Multiply.

1. $6 \cdot 10^3$

_____

2. $22 \cdot 10^1$

_____

3. $8 \cdot 10^2$

_____

4. $18 \cdot 10^0$

_____

5. $70 \cdot 10^2$

_____

6. $25 \cdot 10^3$

_____

7. $3 \cdot 10^4$

_____

8. $180 \cdot 10^3$

_____

9. $84 \cdot 10^4$

_____

10. $315 \cdot 10^2$

_____

11. $210 \cdot 10^3$

_____

12. $1,004 \cdot 10^3$

_____

13. $1,764 \cdot 10^1$

_____

14. $856 \cdot 10^0$

_____

15. $4,055 \cdot 10^3$

_____

16. $716 \cdot 10^4$

_____

Write each number in scientific notation.

17. 34,000

_____

18. 7,700

_____

19. 2,100,000

_____

20. 404,000

_____

21. 21,000,000

_____

22. 612.00

_____

23. 3,001,000

_____

24. $62.13 \cdot 10^4$

_____

25. Lake Superior covers an area of about 31,700 square miles. Write this number in scientific notation.

_____

26. Mars is about $1.42 \cdot 10^8$ miles from the sun. Write this number in standard form.

_____

27. In 2005, the population of China was about $1.306 \cdot 10^9$. What was the population of China written in standard form?

_____

28. A scientist estimates there are 4,800,000 bacteria in a test tube. How does she record the number using scientific notation?

_____

4

Holt Mathematics

Practice

LESSON 1-5 *Order of Operations*

Simplify each expression.

1. $15 \cdot 3 + 12 \cdot 2$

_____

2. $212 + 21 \div 3$

_____

3. $9 \cdot 3 - 18 \div 3$

_____

4. $65 - 36 \div 3$

_____

5. $100 - 9^2 + 2$

_____

6. $3 \cdot 5 - 45 \div 3^2$

_____

7. $54 \div 6 + 4 \cdot 6$

_____

8. $(6 + 5) \cdot 16 \div 2$

_____

9. $60 - 8 \cdot 12 \div 3$

_____

10. $45 - 3^2 \cdot 5$

_____

11. $52 - (8 \cdot 2 \div 4) + 3^2$

_____

12. $(2^3 + 10 \div 2) \cdot 3$

_____

13. $25 + 7(18 - 4^2)$

_____

14. $(6 \cdot 3 - 12)^2 \div 9 + 7$

_____

15. $4^3 - (3 + 12 \cdot 2 - 9)$

_____

16. $2^4 \div 8 + 5$

_____

17. $(1 + 2)^2 \cdot (3 - 1)^2 \div 2$

_____

18. $(16 \div 4) + 4 \cdot (2^2 - 2)$

_____

19. $2^5 - (3 \cdot 7 - 7)$

_____

20. $75 + 5^2 - (8 - 3)$

_____

21. $9 \cdot 6 - 5(10 - 3)$

_____

22. $96 \div 4 + 5 \cdot 2^2$

_____

23. $(15 - 6)^2 \div 3 - 3^3$

_____

24. $19 - 8 \cdot 5 \div 10 + 6 \div 3$

_____

25. Jared has $32. He buys 5 packs of trading cards that cost
$3 each and a display book that costs $7. Simplify the
expression $32 - (5 \cdot 3 + 7)$ to find out how much money
Jared has left.

_____

26. David buys 3 movie tickets for $6 each and 2 bags of popcorn
for $2 each. Simplify the expression $3 \cdot 6 + 2 \cdot 2$ to find out how
much money David spent in all.

_____

Holt Mathematics

LESSON 1-6

Practice
Properties

Tell which property is represented.

1. 12 • 14 = 14 • 12

_____

2. 1 • 36 = 36

_____

3. (17 + 36) + 4 = 17 + (36 + 4)

_____

4. 8 • 12 • 5 = 8 • (12 • 5)

_____

Simplify each expression. Justify each step.

5. 4 • 9 • 50

4 • 9 • 50 = _____

= _____

= _____

= _____

6. (33 + 45) + 7

(33 + 45) + 7 = _____

= _____

= _____

= _____

Use the Distributive Property to find each product.

7. 3(26) = _____

= _____

= _____

= _____

8. (18)9 = _____

= _____

= _____

= _____

Holt Mathematics

LESSON 1-7 Practice
Variables and Algebraic Expressions

Evaluate $n - 5$ for each value of n.

1. $n = 8$ **2.** $n = 121$ **3.** $n = 32$ **4.** $n = 59$

_____   _____   _____   _____

Evaluate each expression for the given values of the variable.

5. $3n + 15$ for $n = 4$ **6.** $h \div 12$ for $h = 60$ **7.** $32x - 32$ for $x = 2$

_____   _____   _____

8. $\dfrac{c}{2}$ for $c = 24$ **9.** $(n \div 2)5$ for $n = 14$ **10.** $8p + 148$ for $p = 15$

_____   _____   _____

11. $e^2 - 7$ for $e = 8$ **12.** $3d^2 + d$ for $d = 5$ **13.** $40 - 4k^3$ for $k = 2$

_____   _____   _____

14. $2y - z$ for $y = 21$ and $z = 19$ **15.** $3h^2 + 8m$ for $h = 3$ and $m = 2$

_____   _____

16. $18 \div a + b \div 9$ for $a = 6$ and $b = 45$ **17.** $10x - 4y$ for $x = 14$ and $y = 5$

_____   _____

18. You can find the area of a rectangle with the expression lw where l represents the length and w represents the width. What is the area of the rectangle at right in square feet?

5 ft

2 ft

_____

19. Rita drove an average of 55 mi/h on her trip to the mountains. You can use the expression $55h$ to find out how many miles she drove in h hours. If she drove for 5 hours, how many miles did she drive?

_____

Holt Mathematics

LESSON 1-8

Practice

Translate Words Into Math

Write each phrase as an algebraic expression.

1. 125 decreased by a number

_____

2. 359 more than z

_____

3. the product of a number and 35

_____

4. the quotient of 100 and w

_____

5. twice a number, plus 27

_____

6. 12 less than 15 times x

_____

7. the product of e and 4, divided by 12

_____

8. y less than 18 times 6

_____

9. 48 more than the quotient of a number and 64 _____

10. 500 less than the product of 4 and a number _____

11. the quotient of p and 4, decreased by 320 _____

12. 13 multiplied by the amount 60 minus w _____

13. the quotient of 45 and the sum of c and 17 _____

14. twice the sum of a number and 600 _____

15. There are twice as many flute players as there are trumpet players in the band. If there are n flute players, write an algebraic expression to find out how many trumpet players there are. _____

16. The Nile River is the longest river in the world at 4,160 miles. A group of explorers traveled along the entire Nile in x days. They traveled the same distance each day. Write an algebraic expression to find each day's distance. _____

17. A slice of pizza has 290 calories, and a stalk of celery has 5 calories. Write an algebraic expression to find out how many calories there are in a slices of pizza and b stalks of celery. _____

18. Grant pays 10¢ per minute plus $5 per month for telephone long distance. Write an algebraic expression for m minutes of long-distance calls in one month. _____

Holt Mathematics

LESSON 1-9 Practice
Simplifying Algebraic Expressions

Identify like terms in each list.

1. $3a$ b^2 b^3 $4b^2$ 4 $5a$

_____

2. x x^4 $4x$ $4x^2$ $4x^4$ $3x^2$

_____

3. $6m$ $6m^2$ n^2 $2n$ 2 $4m$ $5n$

_____

4. $12s$ $7s^4$ $9s$ s^2 5 $5s^4$ 2

_____

Simplify. Justify your steps using the Commutative, Associative, and Distributive Properties when necessary.

5. $2p + 22q^2 - p$ **6.** $x^2 + 3x^2 - 4^2$

_____   _____

7. $n^4 + n^3 + 3n - n - n^3$ **8.** $4a + 4b + 2 - 2a + 5b - 1$

_____   _____

9. $32m^2 + 14n^2 - 12m^2 + 5n - 3$ **10.** $2h^2 + 3g - 2h^2 + 2^2 - 3 + 4g$

_____   _____

11. Write an expression for the perimeter of the figure at the right. Then simplify the expression.

_____

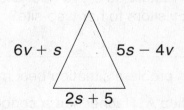

12. Write an expression for the combined perimeters of the figures at the right. Then simplify the expression.

_____

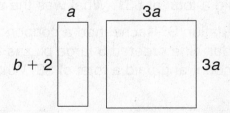

Holt Mathematics

Practice

LESSON 1-10

Equations and Their Solutions

Determine whether the given value of the variable is a solution.

1. $a = 4$ for $12 - a = 6$

2. $m = 37$ for $23 + m = 60$

3. $x = 6$ for $54 = 9x$

_____   _____   _____

4. $g = 96$ for $\frac{g}{4} = 32$

5. $n = 28$ for $n + 44 = 72$

6. $j = 6$ for $84 \div j = 12$

_____   _____   _____

7. $k = 24$ for $3k = 6$

8. $m = 3$ for $42 = m + 39$

9. $y = 8$ for $8y + 6 = 70$

_____   _____   _____

10. $s = 5$ for $18 = 3s - 3$

11. $k = 7$ for $23 - k = 30$

12. $v = 12$ for $84 = 7v$

_____   _____   _____

13. $c = 15$ for $45 - 2c = 15$

14. $x = 10$ for $x + 25 - 2x + 4 = 19$

_____   _____

15. $e = 6$ for $42 = 51 - e$

16. $p = 15$ for $19 = p - 4$

_____   _____

17. Jason and Maya have their own web sites on the Internet. As of last week, Jason's web site had 2,426 visitors. This is twice as many visitors as Maya had. Did Maya have 1,213 visitors or 4,852 visitors to her web site?

_____

18. Which problem situation best matches the equation $3c - 5 = 31$?

Situation A: Rachel had a coupon for $5 off the cost of her order. She ordered 3 large pizzas that each cost the same amount and paid a total of $31. What was the cost of each pizza?

Situation B: Rachel had a coupon for $31 off the cost of her order. She ordered 5 large pizzas that each cost the same amount and paid a total of $3. What was the cost of each pizza?

_____

Holt Mathematics

LESSON 1-11 Practice
Addition and Subtraction Equations

Solve each equation. Check your answer.

1. $33 = y - 44$

2. $r - 32 = 77$

3. $125 = x - 29$

_____

_____

_____

4. $k + 18 = 25$

5. $589 + x = 700$

6. $96 = 56 + t$

_____

_____

_____

7. $a - 9 = 57$

8. $b - 49 = 254$

9. $987 = f - 11$

_____

_____

_____

10. $32 + d = 1,400$

11. $w - 24 = 90$

12. $95 = g - 340$

_____

_____

_____

13. $e - 35 = 59$

14. $84 = v + 30$

15. $h + 15 = 81$

_____

_____

_____

16. $110 = a + 25$

17. $45 + c = 91$

18. $p - 29 = 78$

_____

_____

_____

19. $56 - r = 8$

20. $39 = z + 8$

21. $93 + g = 117$

_____

_____

_____

22. The Morales family is driving from Philadelphia to Boston. So far, they have driven 167 miles. This is 129 miles less than the total distance they must travel. How many miles is Philadelphia from Boston?

_____

23. Ron has $1,230 in his savings account. This is $400 more than he needs to buy a new big screen TV. Write and solve an equation to find out how much the TV costs.

_____

Holt Mathematics

Practice
Multiplication and Division Equations

Solve each equation. Check your answer.

1. $68 = \dfrac{r}{4}$

2. $k \div 24 = 85$

3. $255 = \dfrac{x}{4}$

_____

_____

_____

4. $42 = w \div 18$

5. $\dfrac{a}{15} = 22$

6. $82 = b \div 5$

_____

_____

_____

7. $\dfrac{c}{7} = 9$

8. $28 = z \div 3$

9. $\dfrac{y}{12} = 10$

_____

_____

_____

Solve each equation. Check your answer.

10. $52w = 364$

11. $41x = 492$

12. $410 = 82p$

_____

_____

_____

13. $35d = 735$

14. $195 = 65h$

15. $4k = 140$

_____

_____

_____

16. $110 = 5e$

17. $27a = 216$

18. $96 = 12n$

_____

_____

_____

19. Ashley earns \$5.50 per hour babysitting. She wants to buy a CD
player that costs \$71.50, including tax. How many hours will she
need to work to earn the money for the CD player?

_____

20. A cat can jump the height of up to 5 times the length of its tail.
How high can a cat jump if its tail is 13 inches long?

_____

Holt Mathematics

Practice

LESSON 2-1

Integers

Graph each integer and its opposite on a number line.

1. 8

2. −7

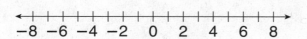

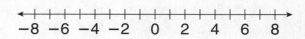

Compare the integers. Use < or >.

3. −15 ☐ −7   **4.** 8 ☐ −8   **5.** −14 ☐ 13   **6.** −18 ☐ −20

Use a number line to order the integers from least to greatest.

7. −1; 4; −5; 7; −3

8. −6; 8; 0; 4; −2

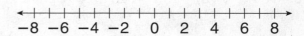

_____

_____

9. 6; 5; −7; −8; −2

10. 1; 3; −4; −5; 7

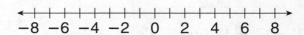

_____

_____

Use a number line to find each absolute value.

11. |−18| _____   **12.** |11| _____   **13.** |−25| _____   **14.** |19| _____

15. |−10| _____   **16.** |16| _____   **17.** |22| _____   **18.** |−14| _____

19. |9| _____   **20.** |−24| _____   **21.** |−7| _____   **22.** |17| _____

23. Christy dove to a depth of 12 feet below the surface of the water. Write the depth as an integer.

_____

24. The highest point in North Carolina is Mt. Mitchell, with a height of 6,684 feet. Write the height of Mt. Mitchell as an integer.

_____

Holt Mathematics

LESSON 2-2 Practice
Adding Integers

Use a number line to find each sum.

1. −1 + 5

2. 4 + (−6)

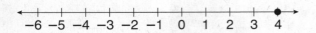

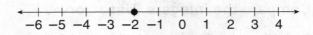

Find each sum.

3. −51 + (−9)

4. 27 + (−6)

5. 1 + (−30)

6. 15 + (−25)

_____

_____

_____

_____

7. 50 + (−7)

8. −19 + (−15)

9. (−23) + 9

10. −19 + (−21)

_____

_____

_____

_____

11. −17 + 11

12. 20 + (−8)

13. (−15) + (−7)

14. 12 + (−14)

_____

_____

_____

_____

Evaluate e + f for the given values.

15. e = 9, f = −24

16. e = −17, f = −7

17. e = 32, f = −19

_____

_____

_____

18. e = −15, f = −15

19. e = −20, f = 20

20. e = −30, f = 12

_____

_____

_____

21. The temperature rose 9°F in 3 hours. If the starting temperature
was −5°F, what was the final temperature?

_____

22. Matt is playing a game. He gains 7 points, loses 10 points, gains
2 points, and then loses 8 points. What is his final score?

_____

Holt Mathematics

Name _____ Date _____ Class _____

Practice
Subtracting Integers

Use a number line to find each difference.

1. $-2 - 3$

2. $5 - (-1)$

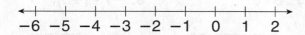

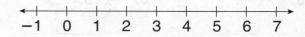

_____

_____

Find each difference.

3. $-6 - 4$

4. $-7 - (-12)$

5. $12 - 16$

6. $5 - (-19)$

_____ _____ _____ _____

7. $-18 - (-18)$

8. $23 - (-23)$

9. $-10 - (-9)$

10. $29 - (-13)$

_____ _____ _____ _____

11. $9 - 15$

12. $-12 - 14$

13. $22 - (-8)$

14. $-16 - (-11)$

_____ _____ _____ _____

Evaluate $x - y$ for each set of values.

15. $x = 14, y = -2$

16. $x = -11, y = 11$

17. $x = -8, y = -15$

_____ _____ _____

18. $x = -9, y = -9$

19. $x = 19, y = -20$

20. $x = 20, y = 25$

_____ _____ _____

21. The high temperature one day was $-1°F$. The low temperature was $-5°F$. What was the difference between the high and low temperatures for the day?

_____

22. The temperature changed from $5°F$ at 6 P.M. to $-2°F$ at midnight. How much did the temperature decrease?

_____

Holt Mathematics

LESSON 2-4 **Practice**

Multiplying and Dividing Integers

Find each product.

1. $8 \cdot (-5)$

2. $-4 \cdot 7$

3. $-6 \cdot (-3)$

4. $-2 \cdot 4$

_____

_____

_____

_____

5. $4 \cdot (-9)$

6. $-9 \cdot 5$

7. $6 \cdot 8$

8. $-7 \cdot (-3)$

_____

_____

_____

_____

Multiply.

9. $-6 \cdot (-6)$

10. $9 \cdot (-3)$

11. $-2 \cdot (-8)$

12. $5 \cdot (-7)$

_____

_____

_____

_____

13. $10 \cdot 8$

14. $-5 \cdot 9$

15. $9 \cdot (-6)$

16. $(-4) \cdot (-11)$

_____

_____

_____

_____

Find each quotient.

17. $25 \div (-5)$

18. $-54 \div (-6)$

19. $-10 \div 5$

20. $-28 \div (-4)$

_____

_____

_____

_____

21. $-42 \div (-7)$

22. $-21 \div 3$

23. $36 \div (-6)$

24. $-81 \div (-9)$

_____

_____

_____

_____

25. $-32 \div 8$

26. $45 \div (-9)$

27. $-72 \div (-8)$

28. $50 \div 10$

_____

_____

_____

_____

29. $-42 \div 6$

30. $-72 \div (-9)$

31. $40 \div 8$

32. $56 \div (-7)$

_____

_____

_____

_____

33. Kim was walking down a rocky path. For 4 minutes, the elevation dropped steadily. Altogether it dropped 8 feet. What was the change in elevation per minute for the 4 minutes?

_____

34. As a front passed, the temperature changed steadily over 6 hours. Altogether it changed -18 degrees. What was the change in temperature per hour for the 6 hours?

_____

Holt Mathematics

LESSON 2-5 Practice

Solving Equations Containing Integers

Solve. Check each answer.

1. $y - 5 = -4$

2. $n - 9 = -14$

3. $13 = x - 15$

_____

_____

_____

4. $p + 18 = 14$

5. $q + 6 = -2$

6. $0 = w + 4$

_____

_____

_____

7. $9h = -36$

8. $-3b = 36$

9. $-100 = -4u$

_____

_____

_____

10. $\dfrac{d}{5} = -7$

11. $\dfrac{c}{4} = -20$

12. $\dfrac{s}{-9} = 9$

_____

_____

_____

13. $f + 15 = -16$

14. $-75 = 3v$

15. $g - 19 = -21$

_____

_____

_____

16. $-63 = -9s$

17. $14 + m = -10$

18. $12 = \dfrac{w}{4}$

_____

_____

_____

19. $x = 15 - 31$

20. $\dfrac{e}{-7} = 8$

21. $-6 = 21 - n$

_____

_____

_____

22. The temperature in Buffalo, New York, was $-2°F$ one day. This
was 42 degrees warmer than the temperature in Nome, Alaska,
on the same day. What was the temperature in Nome?

_____

23. LaSanda bought 20 shares of stock for $175. She sold the stock
for a total profit of $25. What was the selling price of each share
of stock?

_____

Holt Mathematics

Practice
LESSON **2-6** *Prime Factorization*

Tell whether each number is prime or composite.

1. 33   **2.** 41   **3.** 52   **4.** 79

_____   _____   _____   _____

5. 96   **6.** 121   **7.** 83   **8.** 119

_____   _____   _____   _____

Write the prime factorization of each number.

9. 57   **10.** 49   **11.** 88   **12.** 95

_____   _____   _____   _____

13. 105   **14.** 98   **15.** 52   **16.** 42

_____   _____   _____   _____

17. 68   **18.** 91   **19.** 60   **20.** 72

_____   _____   _____   _____

21. 56   **22.** 144   **23.** 370   **24.** 168

_____   _____   _____   _____

25. 124   **26.** 515   **27.** 725   **28.** 220

_____   _____   _____   _____

29. 450   **30.** 1,000   **31.** 1,040   **32.** 2,500

_____   _____   _____   _____

33. The prime factorization of a number is $3^2 \cdot 5 \cdot 11$. What is the number?

_____

Holt Mathematics

LESSON **Practice**
2-7 *Greatest Common Factor*

Find the greatest common factor (GCF).

1. 12, 15

2. 22, 33

3. 63, 45

_____

_____

_____

4. 15, 50

5. 18, 81

6. 18, 48

_____

_____

_____

7. 20, 24

8. 14, 42, 49

9. 3, 6, 9

_____

_____

_____

10. 16, 24, 30

11. 16, 40, 88

12. 42, 70

_____

_____

_____

13. 25, 125, 200

14. 26, 39, 52

15. 36, 100

_____

_____

_____

16. 35, 77

17. 56, 84

18. 14, 49, 56, 84

_____

_____

_____

19. 30, 75, 60, 90

20. 12, 38, 40, 94

21. 48, 66, 96, 102

_____

_____

_____

22. Volunteers are preparing identical backpacks for refugees.
There are 32 maps and 24 dictionaries to use for the backpacks.
What is the greatest number of backpacks they can prepare
using all of the maps and dictionaries?

_____

23. Alyssa is preparing identical fruit baskets. There are 36 oranges
and 60 apples to use for the baskets. What is the greatest
number of fruit baskets she can prepare using all of the oranges
and apples?

_____

Holt Mathematics

Practice
Least Common Multiple

Find the least common multiple (LCM).

1. 8, 10

_____

2. 10, 15

_____

3. 6, 9

_____

4. 12, 16

_____

5. 18, 30

_____

6. 5, 11

_____

7. 15, 45

_____

8. 7, 28

_____

9. 4, 14

_____

10. 3, 10, 12

_____

11. 9, 36, 60

_____

12. 5, 15

_____

13. 7, 14, 49

_____

14. 8, 12, 24, 96

_____

15. 5, 25, 30

_____

16. 5, 9, 18

_____

17. 4, 10, 12, 15

_____

18. 4, 9, 12, 18

_____

19. 4, 12, 24, 36

_____

20. 24, 30, 48, 60

_____

21. 5, 9, 15, 18

_____

22. Jasmine is helping her father plant trees to create a border around the back yard. Jasmine plants a tree every 25 minutes, and her father plants a tree every 15 minutes. If they started together, how long before they would finish planting a tree at the same time?

_____

23. Two dancers are rehearsing in a studio. One dancer's routine lasts 12 minutes. The other dancer's routine lasts 15 minutes. If they start together and take no breaks between their routines, how long before they start together again?

_____

24. Evan and Renzo are swimming laps in the pool. It takes Evan 8 minutes to complete 1 lap and Renzo 6 minutes to complete 1 lap. They start together at the tops of their lanes. In how many minutes will they be together again at the tops of their lanes?

_____

Holt Mathematics

Practice
LESSON 2-9
Equivalent Fractions and Mixed Numbers

Find a fraction equivalent to the given fraction.

1. $\frac{2}{9}$ _____

2. $\frac{8}{15}$ _____

3. $\frac{7}{8}$ _____

4. $\frac{16}{24}$ _____

5. $\frac{12}{20}$ _____

6. $\frac{9}{12}$ _____

Write the fractions with a common denominator.
Then determine if they are equivalent.

7. $\frac{8}{10}$ and $\frac{12}{15}$

8. $\frac{6}{8}$ and $\frac{8}{12}$

9. $\frac{3}{9}$ and $\frac{4}{8}$

_____

_____

_____

10. $\frac{7}{4}$ and $\frac{9}{5}$

11. $\frac{15}{12}$ and $\frac{20}{16}$

12. $\frac{15}{9}$ and $\frac{30}{18}$

_____

_____

_____

Write each as a mixed number.

13. $\frac{21}{8}$ _____

14. $\frac{37}{4}$ _____

15. $\frac{16}{5}$ _____

16. $\frac{49}{9}$ _____

Write each as an improper fraction.

17. $8\frac{2}{3}$ _____

18. $1\frac{7}{12}$ _____

19. $25\frac{3}{4}$ _____

20. $7\frac{5}{6}$ _____

21. Maria's desk is $33\frac{3}{4}$ inches long. Write this number as an improper fraction.

_____

22. Leon walked $\frac{5}{8}$ mile. Liz walked $\frac{10}{16}$ mile. Did they walk the same distance?

_____

Holt Mathematics

Practice

LESSON 2-10

Equivalent Fractions and Decimals

Write each fraction as a decimal. Round to the nearest hundredth, if necessary.

1. $\frac{2}{10}$ _____

2. $\frac{19}{20}$ _____

3. $\frac{5}{8}$ _____

4. $\frac{11}{5}$ _____

5. $\frac{19}{6}$ _____

6. $\frac{17}{4}$ _____

7. $\frac{13}{12}$ _____

8. $\frac{30}{7}$ _____

9. $\frac{7}{4}$ _____

10. $\frac{9}{20}$ _____

11. $\frac{11}{10}$ _____

12. $\frac{2}{25}$ _____

Write each decimal as a fraction in simplest form.

13. 0.85

14. 0.11

15. −0.25

_____

_____

_____

16. 4.3

17. 7.75

18. 5.03

_____

_____

_____

19. −1.06

20. 0.375

21. −2.65

_____

_____

_____

22. −5.6

23. 1.12

24. 0.005

_____

_____

_____

Write each answer as a decimal rounded to the nearest thousandth.

25. In the 1998 Winter Olympics, a total of 205 medals were awarded. The United States won 13 medals. What portion of the medals did the United States win?

_____

26. On a test, Hailey answered 64 out of 75 questions correctly. What portion of her answers was correct?

_____

Holt Mathematics

Practice
LESSON 2-11

Comparing and Ordering Rational Numbers

Compare the fractions. Write < or >. Justify your answer.

1. $-\dfrac{7}{8}$ ☐ $-\dfrac{5}{8}$

2. $\dfrac{3}{10}$ ☐ $\dfrac{3}{8}$

3. $4\dfrac{7}{12}$ ☐ $5\dfrac{5}{12}$

_____ _____ _____

_____ _____ _____

Compare the decimals. Write < or >. Justify your answer.

4. -0.531 ☐ -0.513

5. 0.73 ☐ 0.073

6. $3.\overline{59}$ ☐ 3.599

_____ _____ _____

_____ _____ _____

Order the numbers from least to greatest.

7. $\dfrac{4}{9}$, 0.4, 0.45

8. 1.7, 1.65, $1\dfrac{2}{3}$

9. 3.18, $3\dfrac{1}{8}$, 3.80

_____ _____ _____

10. -5, -5.25, $-5\dfrac{2}{5}$

11. $-6\dfrac{3}{4}$, 6.34, -6.4

12. $\dfrac{11}{12}$, $\dfrac{8}{9}$, 0.91

_____ _____ _____

13. $-\dfrac{3}{5}$, $-\dfrac{5}{7}$, -0.65

14. 0.3, 0.345, $\dfrac{1}{3}$

15. -0.75, $\dfrac{7}{8}$, $-\dfrac{5}{8}$

_____ _____ _____

16. A ream of paper contains 500 sheets of paper. Norm has 373 sheets of paper left from a ream. Express the portion of a ream Norm has as a fraction and as a decimal.

_____

17. The density of Venus, compared to Earth having a density of 1, is 0.943. The density of Mercury is 0.983, compared to the density of Earth. Which planet has a greater density, Venus or Mercury?

_____

Holt Mathematics

LESSON 3-1 Practice
Estimate with Decimals

Estimate by rounding to the nearest integer.

1. 7.45 + 35.84

2. 64.08 − 23.47

3. 6.842 + 14.05

_____

_____

_____

4. 7.156 + 8.34

5. 84.23 + (−78.24)

6. 3.78 − 2.078

_____

_____

_____

7. 46.47 − 98.75

8. 87.24 − 56.38

9. 6.324 + 60.324

_____

_____

_____

10. −28.318 + 18.955

11. 35.082 + 8.37

12. −62.49 − 12.84

_____

_____

_____

Use compatible numbers to estimate.

13. 59.69 ÷ 19.904

14. 86.234 • 9.876

15. 54.87 • 19.47

_____

_____

_____

16. −16.04 • 10.45

17. 31.25 • 6.57

18. 92.67 ÷ 32.89

_____

_____

_____

19. 5.548 • 12.38

20. 88.42 ÷ 7.589

21. 90.05 ÷ 6.21

_____

_____

_____

22. Lisha works 20 hours per week at the bowling alley and makes
$8.55 an hour. She gets a raise of $1.30 an hour. Approximately
how much more will she make each week with her raise?

_____

23. Miguel is able to save $87.34 each month. He wants to buy a
guitar that costs $542.45. For about how many months will
Miguel have to save before he can buy the guitar?

_____

Holt Mathematics

Name _____ Date _____ Class _____

LESSON 3-2 Practice
Adding and Subtracting Decimals

Add. Estimate to check whether each answer is reasonable.

1. 6.14 + 8.91

2. 4.51 + 13.08

3. 12.54 + 21.08

_____

_____

_____

4. 34.22 + (−18.5)

5. −10.10 + (−5.9)

6. 6.87 + (−31.6)

_____

_____

_____

7. 9 + 5.68

8. −15.51 + 8.55

9. 36.36 + 54.54

_____

_____

_____

Subtract.

10. 6.23 − 3.62

11. 8.67 − 6.87

12. 28.94 − 9.48

_____

_____

_____

13. 23.57 − 6.84

14. 16.61 − 7.56

15. 32.08 − 12.37

_____

_____

_____

16. 19 − 6.92

17. 42 − 31.89

18. 23 − 21.45

_____

_____

_____

19. 46.2 − 0.27

20. 22 − 18.63

21. 58.9 − 29.58

_____

_____

_____

22. Anna swims the length of the pool in 38.45 seconds and then swims the length of the pool again in 42.38 seconds. What is her total time for 2 lengths of the pool?

_____

23. Po has 2 gerbils named Yip and Yap. Yip weighs 3.62 ounces, and Yap weighs 2.79 ounces. How much heavier is Yip than Yap?

_____

Holt Mathematics

LESSON 3-3 Practice
Multiplying Decimals

Multiply.

1. 6 • 0.3

2. 3 • 0.05

3. 0.7 • 4

_____ _____ _____

4. 8 • 6.1

5. 7.4 • 6

6. 1.4 • 9

_____ _____ _____

7. 4.8 • 7

8. 3 • 8.2

9. 5.5 • 8

_____ _____ _____

10. 1.5 • 6

11. 7.9 • 2

12. 5 • 6.9

_____ _____ _____

Multiply. Estimate to check whether each answer is reasonable.

13. 6.3 • 7.8

14. 9.7 • (−4.7)

15. 6.8 • 0.9

_____ _____ _____

16. 2.8 • 8.2

17. −7 • 6.42

18. 1.9 • 7.22

_____ _____ _____

19. −5.3 • (−8.4)

20. 7.16 • 0.03

21. 1.56 • (−7.8)

_____ _____ _____

22. 4.6 • 3.1

23. 0.62 • 1.45

24. −5.74 • 1.9

_____ _____ _____

25. Jordan jogged 4.8 miles each day for 21 days last month.
How many miles did she jog last month?

_____

Holt Mathematics

LESSON 3-4 Practice

Dividing Decimals by Integers

Divide. Estimate to check whether each answer is reasonable.

1. $20.8 \div 8$

2. $54.4 \div 5$

3. $0.876 \div 6$

_____

_____

_____

4. $65.6 \div 4$

5. $-96.88 \div 7$

6. $50.4 \div 18$

_____

_____

_____

7. $67.42 \div 4$

8. $88.65 \div (-3)$

9. $77.25 \div 5$

_____

_____

_____

10. $-0.18 \div 4$

11. $41.17 \div (-23)$

12. $74.55 \div 25$

_____

_____

_____

13. $0.144 \div 4$

14. $5.36 \div (-8)$

15. $27.6 \div 12$

_____

_____

_____

16. $22.08 \div (-3)$

17. $1.976 \div 13$

18. $25.56 \div (-5)$

_____

_____

_____

19. $0.504 \div 9$

20. $170.1 \div 27$

21. $5.25 \div (-3)$

_____

_____

_____

22. Doris collects wicker baskets. She spent $9.56 on 3 baskets at the flea market. Then she found 4 more baskets at a garage sale. She paid $10.67 for those baskets. What was the average price per basket for all 7 baskets?

_____

23. As of January 2002, 3 top college football coaches had the following winning percents in bowl games: 0.740, 0.692, and 0.683. What was their average winning percent?

_____

Holt Mathematics

LESSON 3-5 Practice
Dividing Decimals and Integers by Decimals

Divide.

1. $6 \div 0.25$

2. $78.74 \div 12.7$

3. $734.8 \div -1.67$

_____

_____

_____

4. $56.525 \div 0.85$

5. $44.22 \div (-6.7)$

6. $-6.46 \div 0.04$

_____

_____

_____

Divide. Estimate to check whether your answer is reasonable.

7. $63 \div (-4.5)$

8. $8 \div 3.2$

9. $87 \div 7.25$

_____

_____

_____

10. $-36 \div 1.6$

11. $42 \div 4.8$

12. $90 \div 0.36$

_____

_____

_____

13. Freddie used 6.75 gallons of gas to drive
155.25 miles. What was his car's gas mileage?   _____

14. The members of a book club met at a restaurant
for dinner. The total bill was $112.95 and they
shared the bill equally. Each person paid $12.55.
How many members are there in the book club?   _____

Holt Mathematics

Practice

Solving Equations Containing Decimals

Solve.

1. $t + 0.77 = 9.3$

2. $p - 1.34 = -11.8$

3. $r + 2.14 = 7.8$

4. $3.65 + e = -1.4$

5. $w - 16.7 = 8.27$

6. $z - 17.2 = 7.13$

7. $p - 67.5 = 24.81$

8. $h + 26.9 = 12.74$

9. $k + 89.2 = -47.62$

10. $x - 0.45 = 5.97$

11. $1.08 + n = 15.72$

12. $y - 6.32 = 0.73$

13. $4.3p = 28.81$

14. $7.7j = 76.23$

15. $3.8g = -104.12$

16. $18.36 = 2.7y$

17. $99.96 = 6.8x$

18. $293.92 = 17.6c$

19. $\dfrac{e}{7.4} = 6.9$

20. $\dfrac{f}{12.7} = 15.6$

21. $\dfrac{d}{9.7} = 20.8$

22. $\dfrac{w}{-0.2} = 15.4$

23. $\dfrac{m}{9.8} = 1.7$

24. $\dfrac{s}{14.35} = -5.2$

25. Jeff paid a flat fee of $269.50 for a year's worth of vet visits for his 4 cats. He made 14 visits during the year. What was the average cost per visit?

_____

Holt Mathematics

Practice

LESSON 3-7

Estimate with Fractions

Estimate each sum or difference.

1. $\dfrac{5}{11} + \dfrac{4}{9}$

2. $\dfrac{6}{13} + \dfrac{8}{9}$

3. $\dfrac{9}{10} - \dfrac{4}{9}$

_____ _____ _____

4. $1\dfrac{5}{8} - \dfrac{4}{7}$

5. $3\dfrac{7}{8} + \left(-\dfrac{2}{5}\right)$

6. $\dfrac{8}{9} - \dfrac{1}{12}$

_____ _____ _____

7. $4\dfrac{5}{16} + 2\dfrac{9}{10}$

8. $11\dfrac{3}{7} - 5\dfrac{5}{6}$

9. $7\dfrac{1}{16} + \left(-\dfrac{11}{12}\right)$

_____ _____ _____

Estimate each product or quotient.

10. $12\dfrac{2}{5} \div 5\dfrac{3}{4}$

11. $7\dfrac{7}{8} \cdot 4\dfrac{3}{5}$

12. $5\dfrac{1}{6} \cdot 3\dfrac{2}{9}$

_____ _____ _____

13. $23\dfrac{7}{10} \div 4\dfrac{2}{5}$

14. $17\dfrac{11}{12} \div 8\dfrac{5}{9}$

15. $8\dfrac{7}{12} \cdot 6\dfrac{9}{10}$

_____ _____ _____

16. $12\dfrac{3}{8} \cdot 6\dfrac{1}{6}$

17. $35\dfrac{2}{3} \div 3\dfrac{5}{7}$

18. $16\dfrac{5}{8} \cdot 2\dfrac{1}{5}$

_____ _____ _____

19. A hallway has a length of $15\dfrac{3}{4}$ feet and a width of $4\dfrac{1}{12}$ feet. Estimate the area of the hallway in square feet.

_____

20. A 6-week old puppy weighed $8\dfrac{7}{16}$ pounds. At 12 weeks of age, the same puppy weighed about $17\dfrac{3}{8}$ pounds. Estimate how much weight the puppy gained between the ages of 6 weeks and 12 weeks.

_____

30

Holt Mathematics

LESSON **Practice**

3-8 *Adding and Subtracting Fractions*

Add or subtract. Write each answer in simplest form.

1. $\frac{1}{5} + \frac{2}{5}$

2. $\frac{4}{15} + \frac{8}{15}$

3. $\frac{7}{12} - \frac{5}{12}$

4. $\frac{9}{10} - \frac{7}{10}$

5. $\frac{7}{12} - \frac{11}{12}$

6. $\frac{2}{7} + \frac{6}{7}$

7. $\frac{11}{15} + \frac{7}{15}$

8. $\frac{3}{16} - \frac{1}{16}$

9. $\frac{8}{21} + \frac{5}{21}$

10. $\frac{4}{5} - \frac{3}{4}$

11. $\frac{3}{8} + \frac{1}{2}$

12. $\frac{2}{5} - \frac{21}{25}$

13. $\frac{11}{12} + \frac{5}{6}$

14. $\frac{7}{8} - \frac{5}{12}$

15. $\frac{9}{10} + \frac{5}{6}$

16. $\frac{2}{5} - \frac{7}{8}$

17. $\frac{5}{6} + \frac{11}{15}$

18. $\frac{3}{4} - \frac{8}{15}$

19. The school track is $\frac{7}{8}$ mile in length. Sherri ran $\frac{2}{3}$ mile. How much farther does she have to go to get all the way around the track?

20. The Millers budget $\frac{1}{2}$ of their income for fixed expenses and $\frac{1}{8}$ of their income for savings. What fraction of their income is left?

Holt Mathematics

LESSON 3-9 Practice

Adding and Subtracting Mixed Numbers

Add. Write each answer in simplest form.

1. $7\frac{2}{7} + 6\frac{5}{7}$

2. $5\frac{4}{9} + 3\frac{7}{9}$

3. $4\frac{1}{3} + 8\frac{1}{4}$

_____

_____

_____

4. $2\frac{7}{15} + 3\frac{11}{15}$

5. $6\frac{9}{10} + 1\frac{2}{5}$

6. $2\frac{3}{5} + 1\frac{11}{20}$

_____

_____

_____

7. $5\frac{9}{10} + 2\frac{5}{8}$

8. $2\frac{11}{12} + 3\frac{7}{8}$

9. $1\frac{2}{3} + 5\frac{7}{9}$

_____

_____

_____

Subtract. Write each answer in simplest form.

10. $7\frac{7}{9} - 3\frac{5}{9}$

11. $9\frac{7}{10} - 5\frac{3}{10}$

12. $4\frac{13}{15} - 1\frac{7}{15}$

_____

_____

_____

13. $6\frac{2}{3} - 3\frac{3}{5}$

14. $10\frac{3}{4} - 6\frac{1}{3}$

15. $2\frac{3}{10} - 1\frac{7}{8}$

_____

_____

_____

16. $8\frac{7}{12} - 6\frac{1}{3}$

17. $5\frac{7}{8} - 3\frac{9}{10}$

18. $7\frac{6}{7} - 6\frac{3}{4}$

_____

_____

_____

19. Tucker ran $5\frac{3}{8}$ miles on Monday and $3\frac{3}{4}$ miles on Tuesday.
How far did he run on both days?

_____

Holt Mathematics

LESSON **Practice**
3-10 *Multiplying Fractions and Mixed Numbers*

Multiply. Write each answer in simplest form.

1. $5 \cdot \frac{1}{2}$

2. $9 \cdot \frac{3}{4}$

3. $6 \cdot -\frac{2}{5}$

_____

_____

_____

4. $\frac{9}{15} \cdot \frac{5}{7}$

5. $\frac{9}{14} \cdot -\frac{7}{9}$

6. $\frac{7}{12} \cdot \frac{6}{14}$

_____

_____

_____

7. $-12 \cdot \frac{3}{7}$

8. $15 \cdot \frac{5}{6}$

9. $21 \cdot \frac{3}{8}$

_____

_____

_____

10. $2\frac{1}{3} \cdot \frac{3}{5}$

11. $3\frac{2}{5} \cdot \frac{1}{2}$

12. $4\frac{5}{6} \cdot \frac{2}{5}$

_____

_____

_____

13. $2\frac{2}{5} \cdot \frac{2}{3}$

14. $3\frac{3}{4} \cdot \frac{2}{5}$

15. $8\frac{1}{6} \cdot \frac{3}{7}$

_____

_____

_____

16. $2\frac{1}{3} \cdot 3\frac{3}{8}$

17. $1\frac{3}{5} \cdot 6\frac{2}{3}$

18. $2\frac{2}{5} \cdot 4\frac{5}{6}$

_____

_____

_____

19. Rolf spent 15 hours last week practicing his saxophone. If $\frac{3}{10}$ of the time was spent practicing warm-up routines, how much time did he spend practicing warm-up routines?

_____

20. A muffin recipe calls for $\frac{2}{5}$ tablespoon of vanilla extract for 6 muffins. Arthur is making 18 muffins. How much vanilla extract does he need?

_____

Holt Mathematics

LESSON 3-11 Practice

Dividing Fractions and Mixed Numbers

Divide. Write each answer in simplest form.

1. $4 \div \frac{1}{2}$

2. $\frac{1}{5} \div \frac{1}{4}$

3. $\frac{1}{3} \div \frac{3}{5}$

_____ _____ _____

4. $\frac{8}{9} \div \frac{2}{3}$

5. $-\frac{3}{8} \div \frac{3}{4}$

6. $\frac{7}{10} \div \frac{3}{5}$

_____ _____ _____

7. $\frac{5}{12} \div \frac{2}{5}$

8. $\frac{3}{4} \div \frac{4}{9}$

9. $\frac{7}{12} \div \frac{3}{4}$

_____ _____ _____

10. $-4\frac{1}{6} \div \frac{1}{3}$

11. $3\frac{1}{4} \div \frac{2}{5}$

12. $6\frac{1}{9} \div \frac{1}{6}$

_____ _____ _____

13. $2\frac{1}{4} \div 1\frac{3}{4}$

14. $3\frac{3}{4} \div 2\frac{5}{6}$

15. $5\frac{1}{3} \div -1\frac{4}{5}$

_____ _____ _____

16. $2\frac{1}{2} \div 2\frac{1}{3}$

17. $-1\frac{3}{4} \div 1\frac{1}{4}$

18. $7\frac{2}{3} \div 1\frac{1}{5}$

_____ _____ _____

19. Burger Barn has $46\frac{2}{3}$ pounds of ground beef. How many $\frac{1}{3}$-pound burgers can be made using all the ground beef?

_____

20. Roberto needs some roofing tiles to be cut from a large tile. How many tiles that are each $14\frac{3}{8}$ inches in length can he cut from a larger piece of tile that is $100\frac{5}{8}$ inches long?

_____

Holt Mathematics

LESSON 3-12 Practice
Solving Equations Containing Fractions

Solve. Write each answer in simplest form.

1. $t - \frac{3}{7} = \frac{4}{7}$

_____

2. $g - \frac{5}{16} = \frac{3}{16}$

_____

3. $k - \frac{3}{10} = \frac{2}{5}$

_____

4. $n + \frac{1}{7} = \frac{2}{3}$

_____

5. $j + \frac{5}{6} = \frac{17}{18}$

_____

6. $f + \frac{5}{12} = \frac{3}{4}$

_____

7. $\frac{1}{4}s = \frac{3}{4}$

_____

8. $\frac{1}{5}a = \frac{1}{2}$

_____

9. $\frac{4}{5}h = \frac{8}{9}$

_____

10. $p - \frac{2}{3} = \frac{5}{8}$

_____

11. $d - \frac{3}{5} = \frac{7}{10}$

_____

12. $y - \frac{2}{7} = 3\frac{1}{4}$

_____

13. $c + \frac{5}{12} = 2\frac{1}{6}$

_____

14. $w + \frac{4}{15} = 3\frac{1}{3}$

_____

15. $z + \frac{6}{7} = 2\frac{3}{5}$

_____

16. $\frac{5}{6}m = \frac{8}{9}$

_____

17. $\frac{1}{2}x = 3\frac{7}{15}$

_____

18. $\frac{1}{5}r = 2\frac{2}{3}$

_____

19. Sarabeth ran $1\frac{2}{5}$ miles on a path around the park. This was $\frac{5}{8}$ of the distance around the park. What is the distance around the park?

_____

20. An interior decorator bought $12\frac{1}{2}$ yards of material to make drapes. He used $8\frac{2}{3}$ yards on 1 pair of drapes. How much material does he have left?

_____

Holt Mathematics

LESSON 4-1 Practice

The Coordinate Plane

Identify the quadrant that contains each point.

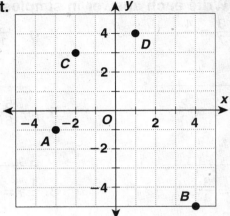

1. A _____

2. B _____

3. C _____

4. D _____

Plot each point on a coordinate plane.

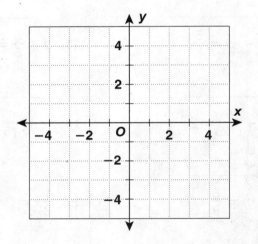

5. $(-4, 0)$

6. $(3, -3)$

7. $(1, 4)$

8. $(-5, -1)$

9. $(-2, 2)$

10. $(-1, -4)$

Give the coordinates of each point.

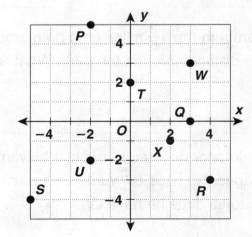

11. P _____

12. Q _____

13. R _____

14. S _____

15. T _____

16. U _____

17. W _____

18. X _____

Holt Mathematics

LESSON **Practice**
4-2 *Tables and Graphs*

Write each ordered pair from the table.

1.

x	y
−12	−8
−9	−4
−6	0
−3	4

→
→
→
→

(x, y)

Graph the ordered pairs from the table.

2.

x	y
−5	4
−3	3
−1	2
1	1

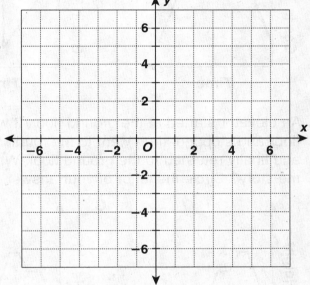

3. The table shows the cost of buying different numbers of souvenir pens. Graph the data.

Number of Pens	Total Cost
1	$2
2	$4
3	$6
4	$8

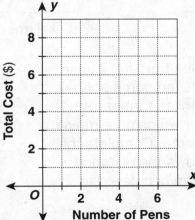

What appears to be the relationship between the number of pens and total cost?

_____

Holt Mathematics

LESSON 4-3

Practice
Interpreting Graphs

1. The gas tank in Karen's car was full. Karen drove the car until only $\frac{1}{4}$ of the tank was full. Karen filled up the tank again and drove the car until $\frac{1}{4}$ of the tank was full. Which graph best shows the story? Circle the letter of your answer.

A 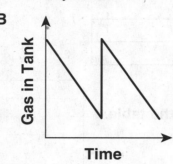   **B** 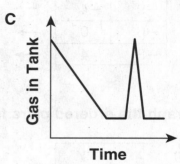   **C**

2. An elevator started at the ground floor. It went up to the sixth floor and stopped, then went to the fourth floor and stopped, and finally returned to the ground floor. Which graph best shows the story? Circle the letter of your answer.

F 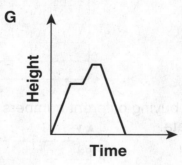   **G** 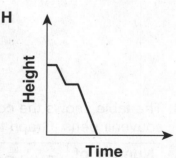   **H**

3. Maxine biked 6 miles from her house to the park. She played some softball. Then she biked 4 miles farther to the movie theater. After watching a movie, Maxine returned home. Complete the graph so that it shows the distance Maxine is from home compared to the time.

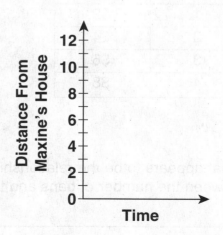

4. Use your graph to find the total number of miles Maxine biked.

_____

Holt Mathematics

LESSON 4-4

Practice

Functions, Tables, and Graphs

Find the output for each input.

1. $y = 5x - 1$

Input	Rule	Output
x	5x − 1	y
−2		
0		
3		
6		

2. $y = -2x^2$

Input	Rule	Output
x	−2x²	y
−2		
2		
3		
4		

Make a function table, and graph the resulting ordered pairs.

3. $y = x \div 4$

Input	Rule	Output	Ordered Pair
x	x ÷ 4	y	(x, y)
−4			
0			
2			
4			

4. $y = x^2 - 5$

Input	Rule	Output	Ordered Pair
x	x² − 5	y	(x, y)
−2			
−1			
0			
1			

Holt Mathematics

Practice
Find a Pattern in Sequences

Tell whether each sequence of *y*-values is arithmetic or geometric. Then find *y* when *n* = 5.

1.

n	1	2	3	4	5
y	−5	10	25	40	■

_____

2.

n	1	2	3	4	5
y	14	28	56	112	■

_____

3.

n	1	2	3	4	5
y	4	12	36	108	■

_____

4.

n	1	2	3	4	5
y	28	42	56	70	■

_____

Write a function that describes each sequence.

5. 12, 24, 36, 48, ...

_____

6. 13, 14, 15, 16, ...

_____

7. −8, −7, −6, −5, ...

_____

8. 2.5, 3.5, 4.5, 5.5, ...

_____

9. 9, 18, 27, 36, ...

_____

10. −12, −11, −10, −9, ...

_____

11. $\frac{3}{4}$, $1\frac{3}{4}$, $2\frac{3}{4}$, $3\frac{3}{4}$, ...

_____

12. −3, −6, −9, −12, ...

_____

13. Mike ran 4 km on Sunday, 6 km on Monday, and 8 km on Tuesday. Write a function that describes the sequence. Then use the function to predict how many kilometers Mike will run on Friday.

_____

Holt Mathematics

LESSON **Practice**
4-6 *Graphing Linear Functions*

Graph each linear function.

1. $y = -x - 5$

Input	Linear Equation	Output	Ordered Pair
x	$y = -x - 5$	**y**	**(x, y)**
−4			
−2			
0			

2. $y = 2x - 1$

Input	Linear Equation	Output	Ordered Pair
x	$y = 2x - 1$	**y**	**(x, y)**
−2			
0			
1			

3. The temperature of a swimming pool is 75°F. When the pool heater is turned on, the temperature rises 2°F every hour. What will the temperature be after 3 hours? Make a function table to answer the question.

_____

4. Mel's Pizza Place charges $15.00 for a large cheese pizza plus $1.25 for each additional topping. What will be the cost of a large pizza with 3 additional toppings? Make a function table to answer the question.

_____

Holt Mathematics

Name _____ Date _____ Class _____

The annual dog show has 22 collies, 28 boxers, and 18 poodles. Write each ratio in all three forms.

1. collies to poodles

2. boxers to collies

_____

3. poodles to boxers

4. poodles to collies

_____

The Franklin School District has 15 art teachers, 27 math teachers, and 18 Spanish teachers. Write the given ratio in all three forms.

5. art teachers to math teachers

6. math teachers to Spanish teachers

_____

7. Spanish teachers to all teachers

8. art and math teachers to Spanish teachers

_____

9. Thirty-two students are asked whether the school day should be longer. Twenty-four vote "no" and 8 vote "yes." Write the ratio of "no" votes to "yes" votes in simplest form.

10. A train car has 64 seats. There are 48 passengers on the train. Write the ratio of seats to passengers in simplest form.

_____

11. Tell whose CD collection has the greater ratio of rock CDs to total CDs.

_____

	Glen	Nina
Classical CDs	4	8
Rock CDs	9	12
Other CDs	5	7

Holt Mathematics

LESSON 5-2 **Practice**

Rates

1. A part-time job pays $237.50 for 25 hours of work. _____
   How much money does the job pay per hour?

2. A class trip consists of 84 students and 6 _____
   teachers. How many students per teacher
   are there?

3. A factory builds 960 cars in 5 days. What is the _____
   average number of cars the factory produces
   per day?

4. The Wireless Cafe charges $5.40 for 45 minutes _____
   of Internet access. How much money does The
   Wireless Cafe charge per minute?

5. A bowler scores 3,152 points in 16 games. _____
   What is his average score in points per game?

6. Melissa drives 238 miles in 5 hours. What is her _____
   average rate of speed?

7. An ocean liner travels 1,233 miles in 36 hours. _____
   What is the ocean liner's average rate of speed?

8. A plane is scheduled to complete a 1,792-mile _____
   flightin 3.5 hours. In order to complete the trip
   on time, what should be the plane's average
   rate of speed?

9. The Nuthouse sells macadamia nuts in three _____
   sizes. The 12 oz jar sells for $8.65, the 16 oz
   jar sells for $10.99, and the 24 oz gift tin costs
   $16.99. Which size is the best buy?

10. Nina paid $37.57 for 13 gallons of gas. Fred paid _____
    $55.67 for 19 gallons of gas. Eleanor paid $48.62
    for 17 gallons of gas. Who got the best buy?

Holt Mathematics

LESSON 5-3 **Practice**
Slope and Rates of Change

Tell whether the slope is positive or negative. Then find the slope.

1.
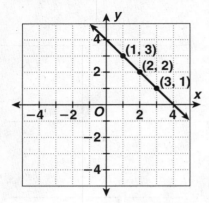

_____ _____

2.
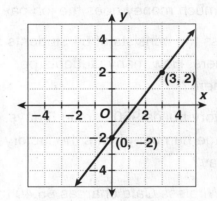

_____ _____

Use the given slope and point to graph each line.

3. $-\frac{1}{2}$; (2,4)

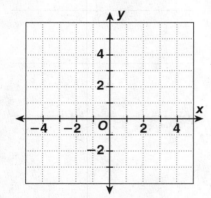

4. $\frac{1}{3}$; (−1,−2)

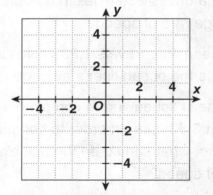

Tell whether each graph shows a constant or variable rate of change.

5.
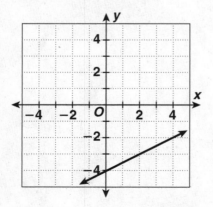

_____

6.
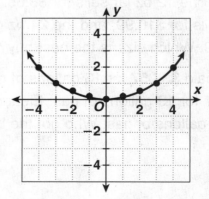

_____

44

Holt Mathematics

Name _____ Date _____ Class _____

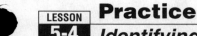

Practice
Identifying and Writing Proportions

Determine whether the ratios are proportional.

1. $\frac{3}{4}, \frac{24}{32}$

2. $\frac{5}{6}, \frac{15}{18}$

3. $\frac{10}{12}, \frac{20}{32}$

_____   _____   _____

4. $\frac{7}{10}, \frac{22}{30}$

5. $\frac{9}{6}, \frac{21}{14}$

6. $\frac{7}{9}, \frac{24}{27}$

_____   _____   _____

7. $\frac{4}{10}, \frac{6}{15}$

8. $\frac{7}{12}, \frac{13}{20}$

9. $\frac{4}{9}, \frac{6}{12}$

_____   _____   _____

10. $\frac{7}{8}, \frac{14}{16}$

11. $\frac{9}{10}, \frac{45}{50}$

12. $\frac{3}{7}, \frac{10}{21}$

_____   _____   _____

Find a ratio equivalent to each ratio. Then use the ratios to write a proportion.

13. $\frac{7}{9}$

14. $\frac{11}{12}$

15. $\frac{14}{15}$

_____   _____   _____

16. $\frac{35}{55}$

17. $\frac{14}{10}$

18. $\frac{25}{18}$

_____   _____   _____

Holt Mathematics

Name _____ Date _____ Class _____

Practice
Solving Proportions

Use cross products to solve each proportion.

1. $\dfrac{2}{5} = \dfrac{x}{35}$

_____

2. $\dfrac{7}{r} = \dfrac{1}{4}$

_____

3. $\dfrac{k}{75} = \dfrac{9}{15}$

_____

4. $\dfrac{1}{3} = \dfrac{z}{27}$

_____

5. $\dfrac{2}{11} = \dfrac{12}{d}$

_____

6. $\dfrac{24}{s} = \dfrac{4}{12}$

_____

7. $\dfrac{w}{42} = \dfrac{6}{7}$

_____

8. $\dfrac{t}{54} = \dfrac{2}{9}$

_____

9. $\dfrac{3}{8} = \dfrac{a}{64}$

_____

10. $\dfrac{17}{34} = \dfrac{7}{f}$

_____

11. $\dfrac{15}{h} = \dfrac{5}{6}$

_____

12. $\dfrac{4}{15} = \dfrac{36}{c}$

_____

13. $\dfrac{z}{25} = \dfrac{12}{5}$

_____

14. $\dfrac{36}{k} = \dfrac{9}{4}$

_____

15. $\dfrac{5}{14} = \dfrac{n}{42}$

_____

16. $\dfrac{8}{9} = \dfrac{40}{m}$

_____

17. $\dfrac{7}{c} = \dfrac{63}{54}$

_____

18. $\dfrac{24}{21} = \dfrac{s}{35}$

_____

19. $\dfrac{e}{22} = \dfrac{6}{15}$

_____

20. $\dfrac{3}{v} = \dfrac{12}{17}$

_____

21. $\dfrac{5}{14} = \dfrac{4}{a}$

_____

22. Eight oranges cost $1.00. How much will 5 dozen oranges cost?

_____

23. A recipe calls for 2 eggs to make 10 pancakes. How many eggs
will you need to make 35 pancakes?

_____

Holt Mathematics

Name _____ Date _____ Class _____

LESSON **Practice**
5-6 *Customary Measurements*

Choose the most appropriate customary unit for each measurement.
Justify your answer.

1. the weight of a paperback book

_____

_____

2. the capacity of a large soup pot

_____

_____

3. the length of a dining room table

_____

_____

4. the weight of an elephant

_____

_____

Convert each measure.

5. 6 mi to feet

_____

6. 104 oz to pounds

_____

7. 12 qt to pints

_____

8. 5,000 lb to tons

_____

9. 48 yd to feet

_____

10. 96 fl oz to pints

_____

11. 6.5 ft to inches

_____

12. 20 qt to gallons

_____

13. $3\frac{1}{4}$ lb to ounces

_____

14. Marina has 2.5 lb of cashews. She puts 6 oz of cashews in a bag and gives the bag to her brother. What weight of cashews does Marina have left?

_____

15. Faye is 5 ft 5 in. Faye is 10 in. shorter than her older brother. How tall is Faye's older brother?

_____

Holt Mathematics

Name _____ Date _____ Class _____

LESSON 5-7 Practice
Similar Figures and Proportions

**Identify the corresponding sides in each pair of triangles.
Then use ratios to determine whether the triangles are similar.**

1.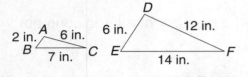

2.
S 3 m   V   9 m
5 m   R   15 m   U
       3 m
T   9 m
              W

_____

_____

3.
X 10 cm
       Y
30 cm   K 20 cm J
       25 cm   8 cm
                24 cm   L
Z

4.
       E   20 ft P
15 ft   16 ft Q   21 ft
F 13 ft G   16 ft
                    R

_____

_____

_____

_____

**Use the properties of similarity to determine whether the
figures are similar.**

5.
   24 yd
A   B   E   36 yd   F
28 yd   42 yd
D   C   H   G

6.
R   5 cm   S   K   5 cm   L
100° 80°   110° 70°
5 cm   5 cm   5 cm   5 cm
80° 100°   70° 110°
U   5 cm   T   N   5 cm   M

_____

_____

_____

_____

Holt Mathematics

LESSON 5-8 **Practice**
Using Similar Figures

$\triangle ABC \sim \triangle DEF$ in each pair. Find the unknown lengths.

1.
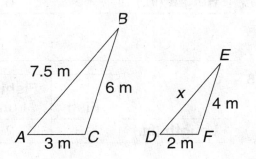

21 cm A 27 cm
B ___ C
36 cm

D
35 cm   45 cm
E ___ F
x

_____

2.
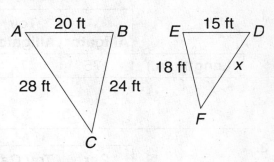

A 20 ft B
28 ft   24 ft
C

E 15 ft D
18 ft   x
F

_____

3.
B
7.5 m   6 m
A ___ C
3 m

E
x   4 m
D ___ F
2 m

_____

4.
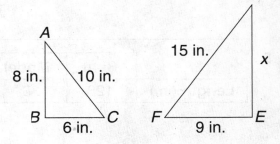

A
8 in.   10 in.
B ___ C
6 in.

D
15 in.   x
F ___ E
9 in.

_____

5. The two rectangular picture frames at
the right are similar. What is the height
of the larger picture frame?

| 2 ft
|_ 3 ft _|

| ?
|_ 4.2 ft _|

_____

6. A palm tree casts a shadow that is 44
feet long. A 6-foot ladder casts a
shadow that is 16 feet long. Use
Estimate the height of the palm tree.

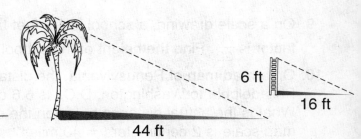

6 ft
16 ft

44 ft

_____

Holt Mathematics

Name _____ Date _____ Class _____

Practice
Scale Drawings and Scale Models

Identify the scale factor.

1.

	Alligator	Toy Alligator
Length (in.)	175	7

2.

	Airplane	Model
Length (ft)	24	3

3.

	Car	Toy Car
Length (ft)	13.5	1.5

4.

	Person	Action Figure
Height (in.)	66	6

5.

	Boat	Model
Length (in.)	128	8

6.

	Fish	Fishing Lure
Length (in.)	18	2

7.

	Tiger	Stuffed Animal
Length (in.)	70	14

8.

	House	Dollhouse
Height (ft)	39.2	2.8

9. On a scale drawing, a school is 1.6 feet tall. The scale factor is $\frac{1}{22}$. Find the height of the school.

10. On a road map of Pennsylvania, the distance from Philadelphia to Washington, D.C., is 6.8 centimeters. What is the actual distance between the cities if the map scale is 2 centimeters = 40 miles?

11. On a scale drawing, a bicycle is $6\frac{4}{5}$ inches tall. The scale factor is $\frac{1}{6}$. Find the height of the bicycle.

Holt Mathematics

Name _____ Date _____ Class _____

Practice
Percents

Write the percent modeled by each grid.

1.
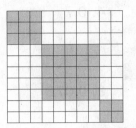

2.
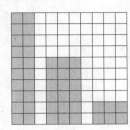

3.
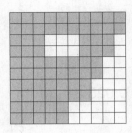

_____   _____   _____

Write each percent as a fraction in simplest form.

4. 16%   **5.** 49%   **6.** 20%   **7.** 15%

_____   _____   _____   _____

8. 18%   **9.** 60%   **10.** 35%   **11.** 46%

_____   _____   _____   _____

12. 86%   **13.** 79%   **14.** 56%   **15.** 45%

_____   _____   _____   _____

Write each percent as a decimal.

16. 33%   **17.** 57%   **18.** 46%   **19.** 6%

_____   _____   _____   _____

20. 4.7%   **21.** 13.2%   **22.** 75.8%   **23.** 4%

_____   _____   _____   _____

24. 1.16%   **25.** 27.05%   **26.** 93.01%   **27.** 7.9%

_____   _____   _____   _____

Holt Mathematics

Name _____ Date _____ Class _____

Practice
Fractions, Decimals, and Percents

Write each decimal as a percent.

1. 0.17   **2.** 0.56   **3.** 0.04   **4.** 0.7

_____   _____   _____   _____

5. 0.025   **6.** 0.803   **7.** 0.3   **8.** 0.072

_____   _____   _____   _____

Write each fraction as a percent.

9. $\frac{13}{40}$ **10.** $\frac{3}{5}$ **11.** $\frac{3}{20}$ **12.** $\frac{5}{12}$

_____   _____   _____   _____

13. $\frac{5}{16}$ **14.** $\frac{3}{80}$ **15.** $\frac{5}{6}$ **16.** $\frac{19}{25}$

_____   _____   _____   _____

Decide whether pencil and paper, mental math, or a calculator is most useful when solving the following problems. Then solve.

17. In a survey, 60 baseball fans were asked whether they thought the designated hitter rule should be changed. Forty-one fans thought the rule should be changed. What percent of the fans surveyed said that the designated hitter rule should be changed?

_____

_____

18. The police use a speed gun to monitor one part of a highway. During one hour, 6 out of 25 cars were traveling above the speed limit. What percent of the cars were traveling above the speed limit?

_____

_____

Holt Mathematics

Name _____ Date _____ Class _____

LESSON **Practice**
6-3 *Estimate with Percents*

Use a fraction to estimate the percent of each number.

1. 21% of 82

2. 35% of 42

3. 47% of 164

4. 9% of 68

_____

_____

_____

_____

5. 65% of 78

6. 11% of 92

7. 26% of 124

8. 89% of 51

_____

_____

_____

_____

9. 77% of 198

10. 5% of 75

11. 31% of 148

12. 53% of 539

_____

_____

_____

_____

13. In 2004, about $38 out of every $100 spent on advertising was spent on television advertising. The amount spent on radio advertising was about 21% as much as was spent on television advertising. How much of every $100 spent on advertising was spent on radio advertising?

_____

Use 1% or 10% to estimate the percent of each number.

14. 32% of 46

15. 81% of 36

16. 15% of 44

17. 21% of 62

_____

_____

_____

_____

18. 3% of 72

19. 62% of 88

20. 12% of 48

21. 65% of 124

_____

_____

_____

_____

22. 18% of 147

23. 5% of 837

24. 37% of 213

25. 2% of 188

_____

_____

_____

_____

26. The Fresh Acres Swim Club has a $35,000 budget for pool maintenance this year. The club members have agreed to raise the budget by 4%. Estimate the pool maintenance budget for next year.

_____

Holt Mathematics

LESSON 6-4 Practice
Percent of a Number

Find the percent of each number.

1. 25% of 56

2. 10% of 110

3. 5% of 150

4. 90% of 180

_____

_____

_____

_____

5. 125% of 48

6. 225% of 88

7. 2% of 350

8. 285% of 200

_____

_____

_____

_____

9. 150% of 125

10. 46% of 235

11. 78% of 410

12. 0.5% of 64

_____

_____

_____

_____

Find the percent of each number. Check whether your answer is reasonable.

13. 55% of 900

14. 140% of 50

15. 75% of 128

16. 3% of 600

_____

_____

_____

_____

17. 16% of 85

18. 22% of 105

19. 0.7% of 110

20. 95% of 500

_____

_____

_____

_____

21. 3% of 750

22. 162% of 250

23. 18% of 90

24. 23.2% of 125

_____

_____

_____

_____

25. 0.1% of 950

26. 11% of 300

27. 52% of 410

28. 250% of 12

_____

_____

_____

_____

29. The largest frog in the world is the goliath, found in West Africa. This type of frog can grow to be 12 inches long. The smallest frog in the world is about 4% as long as the goliath. What is the approximate length of the smallest frog in the world?

_____

Holt Mathematics

Practice
LESSON 6-5
Solving Percent Problems

1. 50 is 40% of what number?

2. 12 is 25% of what number?

3. 18 is what percent of 60?

4. 12 is what percent of 96?

5. 4% of what number is 25?

6. 80% of what number is 160?

7. What percent of 55 is 22?

8. What percent of 75 is 6?

9. 15 is 30% of what number?

10. 8% of what number is 2?

11. 7 is what percent of 105?

12. 24 is 40% of what number?

13. 10% of what number is 14?

14. 16 is what percent of 200?

15. What percent of 32 is 4?

16. What percent of 150 is 60?

17. 1% of what number is 11?

18. 20% of what number is 14?

19. The sales tax on a $750 computer at J & M Computers is $48.75. What is the sales tax rate?

20. A hardcover book sells for $24 at The Bookmart. Ben pays a total of $25.02 for the book. What is the sales tax rate?

Holt Mathematics

LESSON 6-6 Practice
Percent of Change

Find each percent of change. Round answers to the nearest tenth, if necessary.

1. 20 is decreased to 11 _____   **2.** 24 is increased to 30 _____

3. 56 is decreased to 14 _____   **4.** 25 is increased to 100 _____

5. 18 is increased to 45 _____   **6.** 90 is decreased to 75 _____

7. 126 is decreased to 48 _____   **8.** 65 is increased to 144 _____

9. 42 is increased to 72 _____   **10.** 84 is decreased to 8 _____

11. 95 is increased to 145 _____   **12.** 248 is decreased to 200 _____

13. 105 is decreased to 32 _____   **14.** 75 is increased to 350 _____

15. 93 is decreased to 90 _____   **16.** 16 is decreased to 2 _____

17. A backpack that normally sells for $39 is on sale for 33% off. Find the amount of the discount and the sale price.

_____

18. A sporting goods store is having a closeout on a certain style of running shoes. They are marked 55% off the regular price. The regular price is $79.95. Find the amount of the discount and the sale price.

_____

19. A gallery owner purchased a very old painting for $3,000. The painting sells at a 325% increase in price. What is the retail price of the painting?

_____

20. In August, the Simons' water bill was $48. In September, it was 15% lower. What was the Simons' water bill in September?

_____

Holt Mathematics

LESSON 6-7 Practice
Simple Interest

Find each missing value.

1. $p = \$1,500$, $r = 5\%$, $t = 3$ years

   $I =$ _____

2. $p = \$6,000$, $r = 4\%$, $t = 2$ years

   $I =$ _____

3. $I = \$30$, $r = 4\%$, $t = 2$ years

   $p =$ _____

4. $I = \$180$, $r = 5\%$, $t = 3$ years

   $p =$ _____

5. $I = \$20$, $p = \$250$, $t = 2$ years

   $r =$ _____

6. $I = \$144$, $p = \$800$, $t = 3$ years

   $r =$ _____

7. $p = \$525$, $r = 3\%$, $t = 1$ year

   $I =$ _____

8. $p = \$3,200$, $r = 6\%$, $t = 4$ years

   $I =$ _____

9. $I = \$450$, $r = 6\%$, $t = 4$ years

   $p =$ _____

10. $I = \$1,440$, $r = 3\%$, $t = 5$ years

    $p =$ _____

11. $I = \$1,275$, $p = \$5,100$, $t = 5$ years

    $r =$ _____

12. $I = \$3,920$, $p = \$14,000$, $t = 4$ years

    $r =$ _____

13. $p = \$1,300$, $r = 4.5\%$, $t = 6$ months

    $I =$ _____

14. $I = \$47.25$, $r = 3.5\%$, $t = 1.5$ years

    $p =$ _____

15. $I = \$891$, $p = \$2,700$, $t = 5.5$ years

    $r =$ _____

16. $I = \$126$, $p = \$400$, $t = 9$ years

    $r =$ _____

17. You deposit $2,500 in an account that earns 4% simple interest. How long will it be before the total amount is $3,000? _____

18. You deposit $5,000 in account that earns 6.5% simple interest. How much will be in the account after 3 years? _____

19. A deposit of $10,000 was made to an account the year you were born. After 12 years, the account is worth $16,600. What simple interest rate did the account earn? _____

20. How long will it take for $6,500 to double at a simple interest rate of 7%? Round to the nearest tenth of a year. _____

Holt Mathematics

LESSON 7-1

Practice
Frequency Tables, Stem-and-Leaf Plots, and Line Plots

The table shows the heights of students in Ms. Blaire's class.
Use the table for Exercises 1 and 2.

Height (in.)	
Males	60, 45, 48, 57, 62, 59, 57, 60, 56, 58, 61, 52, 55
Females	49, 52, 56, 48, 51, 60, 47, 53, 55, 58, 54

1. Make a cumulative frequency table of the data.

Heights of Students

Height (in.)	Frequency	Cumulative Frequency

2. How many of the students were less than 60 in tall? _____

3. Make a stem-and-leaf plot of the data.

Height of Students

Stem	Leaves

Key: _____

4. How many of the students were less than 50 in tall? _____

5. Make a line plot of the data.

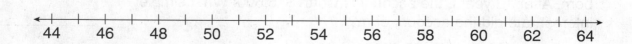

6. Which height occurred the greatest number of times? _____

Holt Mathematics

Name _____ Date _____ Class _____

Practice
7-2 *Mean, Median, Mode, and Range*

Find the mean, median, mode, and range of each data set.

1. 46, 35, 23, 37, 29, 53, 43

_____

2. 72, 56, 47, 69, 75, 48, 56, 57

_____

3. 19, 11, 80, 19, 27, 19, 10, 25, 15

_____

4. 7, 8, 20, 6, 9, 11, 10, 8, 9, 8

_____

5. The line plot shows the number of hours 15 students said they spent on homework in one week. Which measure of central tendency best describes the data? Justify your answer.

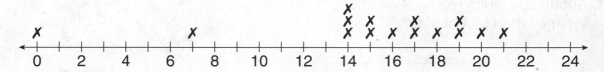

_____

_____

Identify the outlier in each data set. Then determine how the outlier affects the mean, median, and mode of the data. Then tell which measure of central tendency best describes the data with and without the outlier.

6. 14, 16, 13, 15, 5, 16, 12

_____

_____

7. 48, 46, 52, 92, 57, 58, 52, 61, 56

_____

_____

Holt Mathematics

Name _____ Date _____ Class _____

Practice
Bar Graphs and Histograms

The bar graph shows the elevations of the highest points in several states. Use the graph for Exercises 1–3.

1. Which state has the highest elevation?

   _____

2. About how much higher is Granite Peak than Guadalupe Peak?

   _____

3. About how much higher is Mount Whitney than Mount Marcy?

   _____

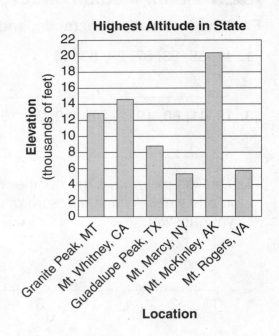

Highest Altitude in State

4. The table shows the approximate mean length and width of three states. Make a double-bar graph of the data.

State	Length (mi)	Width (mi)
Florida	500	160
New York	330	283
Virginia	430	200

5. The list shows the bowling scores of the first game played by a group of bowlers on Thursday night. Make a histogram of the data.
   96, 110, 132, 128, 105, 94, 116, 95, 126, 114, 123, 136, 121, 99

Holt Mathematics

Name _____ Date _____ Class _____

The circle graph directly below shows the results of a survey of 80 teens who were asked about their favorite musical instruments. Use the graph for Exercises 1–3.

Favorite Musical Instruments

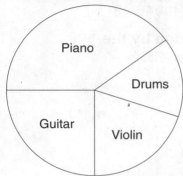

1. Did more teens pick piano or drums?

_____

2. About what percent of teens picked guitar?

_____

3. According to the survey, 20% of teens chose violin. How many teens chose violin?

_____

The circle graph below shows the results of a survey of 100 people who were asked about their favorite vacation destinations. Use the graph for Exercises 4–6.

Favorite Vacation Destinations

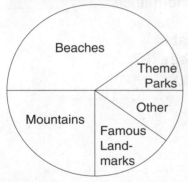

4. Did more people pick mountains or beaches?

_____

5. About what percent of people picked mountains?

_____

6. According to the survey, 15% of the people chose famous landmarks. How many people chose famous landmarks?

_____

Decide whether a bar graph or a circle graph would best display the information. Explain your answer.

7. number of tornadoes in each state during one year

_____

_____

8. the number of pounds of Macintosh apples sold compared with the total number of pounds of apples sold at a market in one day

_____

_____

Holt Mathematics

LESSON 7-5 Practice
Box-and-Whisker Plots

1. Use the data to make a box-and-whisker plot.
   19, 46, 37, 16, 24, 47, 23, 19, 31, 25, 42

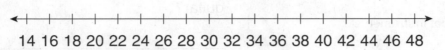

14 16 18 20 22 24 26 28 30 32 34 36 38 40 42 44 46 48

Use the box-and-whisker plot of games won per season by the New York Yankees and the Arizona Diamondbacks for 1998-2005 for Exercises 2-4.

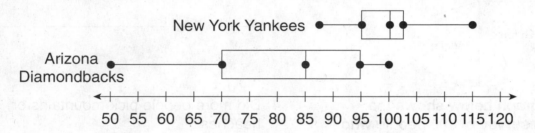

New York Yankees

Arizona Diamondbacks

50 55 60 65 70 75 80 85 90 95 100 105 110 115 120

2. Which team has the greater median number of games won? _____

3. Which team has the greater interquartile range of games won? _____

4. Which team appears to have a more predictable performance? _____

Use the box-and-whisker plot of nightly tip totals that a waitress gets at two different restaurants for Exercises 5-7.

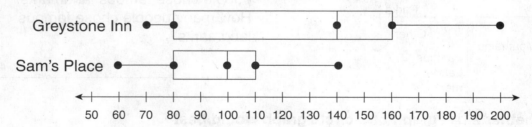

Greystone Inn

Sam's Place

50 60 70 80 90 100 110 120 130 140 150 160 170 180 190 200

5. At which restaurant is the median tip total greater? _____

6. At which restaurant is the interquartile range of tip totals greater?

   _____

7. At which restaurant does the tip total appear to be more predictable?

   _____

Holt Mathematics

Name _____ Date _____ Class _____

Practice
Line Graphs

Use the table for Exercises 1–3.

Retail Price of Regular Gasoline in the United States (to the nearest cent)

Year	1990	1992	1994	1996	1998	2000	2002	2004
Price Per Gallon	$1.16	$1.13	$1.11	$1.23	$1.06	$1.51	$1.32	$1.82

1. Make a line graph of the data.

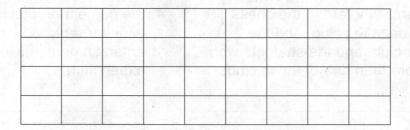

2. When did the cost of gasoline decrease the most?

_____

3. About how much did gasoline cost in 1995?

_____

The table below shows the student population at elementary schools in two cities, New City and Jackson.

Year	1996	1997	1998	1999	2000	2001	2002	2003
New City	450	460	440	430	495	500	600	645
Jackson	500	475	450	525	430	440	485	480

4. Make a double-line graph of the data.

5. During which year did New City's school population increase the most?

_____

6. The mall in Jackson closed. Many people lost their jobs and moved their families to New City, where a new mall opened. In what year did this probably happen? Explain your thinking.

_____

_____

_____

Key:

63

Holt Mathematics

LESSON 7-7

Practice

Choosing an Appropriate Display

Choose the type of graph that would best represent this data.

1. the number of points scored by five different basketball players in a game

_____

2. the distribution of test scores in a math class

_____

_____

3. the students who are in the chess club, the debating club, and the computer club, and the students who are in more than one of those clubs

_____

4. the percent of total income a family uses for rent, food, clothing, entertainment, savings and other expenditures

_____

The table shows the earnings of The Sandman Company during each of five years. Explain why each display does or does not appropriately represent the data.

Year	Earnings (millions of dollars)
2001	1
2002	3
2003	8
2004	12
2005	16

5.

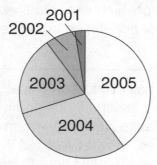

Earnings of The Sandman Company

_____

_____

_____

_____

6.

Earnings of The Sandman Company

_____

_____

_____

_____

Holt Mathematics

LESSON 7-8 Practice

Populations and Samples

1. Determine which sampling method will better represent the entire population. Justify your answer.

Reading Habits of High School Students	
Sampling Method	**Results of Survey**
Dinah surveys 48 students who she knows.	91% have read a novel in the past month.
Suki gives survey forms to 100 students who were randomly chosen from a school attendance list.	59% have read a novel in the past month.

_____

_____

_____

For Problems 2 and 3, determine whether each sample may be biased. Explain.

2. An on-line bookseller randomly chooses 200 book buyers from its database and then surveys those book buyers to find out if they were satisfied with the time it took to deliver their orders.

_____

_____

3. Milena surveys 80 high school students who are leaving a jazz concert to determine the favorite type of music among high school students.

_____

_____

4. Zack chooses a random sample of 50 out of 400 students. He finds that 7 of them have traveled to a foreign country. Zack claims that over 50 of the 400 students have traveled to a foreign country. Do you agree? Explain your answer.

_____

5. A mint produces 150,000 souvenir coins each year. In a random sample of 400 coins, 3 have a misprint. Predict the number of coins that will have misprints in a year.

_____

Holt Mathematics

LESSON 7-9

Practice
Scatter Plots

The table shows boys' average heights in inches from ages 6 through 13. Use the table for Exercises 1–3.

Age	6	7	8	9	10	11	12	13
Height (in.)	$46\frac{3}{4}$	49	51	$53\frac{1}{4}$	$55\frac{1}{4}$	$57\frac{1}{4}$	59	61

1. Make a scatter plot of the data.

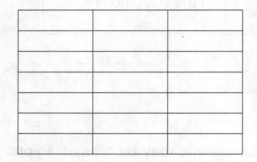

2. Describe the relationship between the data sets.

_____

_____

3. What kind of correlation does the plot show?

_____

_____

Write *positive, negative,* or *no correlation* to describe each relationship.

4.

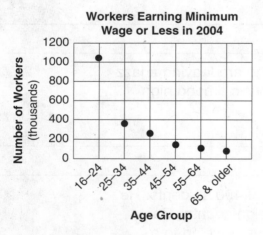

Workers Earning Minimum Wage or Less in 2004

_____

5.

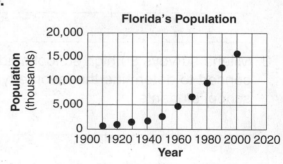

Florida's Population

_____

6. student test scores and the number of students who walk to school

_____

7. the grade levels of students and their ages in months

_____

8. the year a state entered the union and the number of years as a state

_____

9. ages of students and their grades on tests

_____

Holt Mathematics

Practice

LESSON 7-10 Misleading Graphs

1. Which graph could be misleading? Why?

Graph A

Average Life Span of Selected Animals

Graph B

Average Life Span of Selected Animals

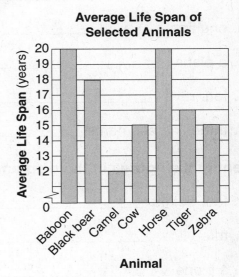

_____

_____

Explain why each graph could be misleading.

2.

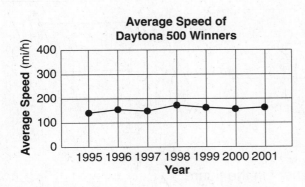

3.

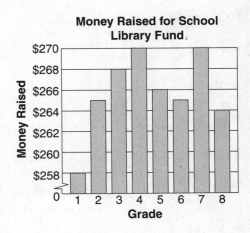

_____   _____

_____   _____

_____   _____

Holt Mathematics

LESSON 8-1 **Practice**
Building Blocks of Geometry

Identify the figures in the diagram.

1. three points _____

2. one line _____

3. a plane _____

4. four rays _____

5. three line segments _____

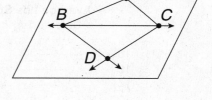

Identify the figures in the diagram.

6. four points _____

7. three lines _____

8. a plane _____

9. three rays _____

10. four line segments _____

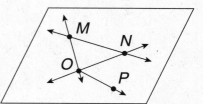

Identify the figures in the diagram.

11. four points _____

12. two lines _____

13. a plane _____

14. four rays _____

15. five line segments _____

16. Identify the line segments that are congruent in the figure.

_____

_____

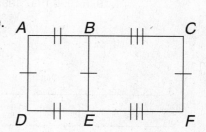

Holt Mathematics

Name _____ Date _____ Class _____

LESSON 8-2 Practice
Classifying Angles

Tell whether each angle is acute, right, obtuse, or straight.

1.

_____

2.

_____

3.

_____

Use the diagram to tell whether the angles are complimentary, supplementary or neither.

4. ∠AQC and ∠GQC

_____

5. ∠BQD and ∠DQE

_____

6. ∠CQE and ∠EQF

_____

7. ∠GQF and ∠FQE

_____

8. ∠BQC and ∠DQC

_____

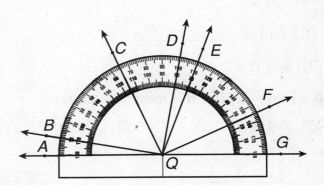

9. Angles W and X are supplementary. If m∠W is 37°, what is m∠X?

_____

10. Angles S and T are complementary. If m∠S is 64°, what is m∠T?

_____

11. Angles C and D are supplementary. If m∠C is 83°, what is m∠D?

_____

12. Angles U and V are complementary. If m∠U is 41°, what is m∠V?

_____

Holt Mathematics

Practice

Angle Relationships

Tell whether the lines appear parallel, perpendicular, or skew.

1. $\overleftrightarrow{AB}$ and $\overleftrightarrow{DE}$ _____

2. $\overleftrightarrow{EF}$ and $\overleftrightarrow{CF}$ _____

3. $\overleftrightarrow{AB}$ and $\overleftrightarrow{AD}$ _____

4. $\overleftrightarrow{BC}$ and $\overleftrightarrow{DE}$ _____

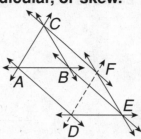

Tell whether the lines appear parallel, perpendicular, or skew.

5. $\overleftrightarrow{BD}$ and $\overleftrightarrow{DG}$ _____

6. $\overleftrightarrow{AB}$ and $\overleftrightarrow{BD}$ _____

7. $\overleftrightarrow{DG}$ and $\overleftrightarrow{IJ}$ _____

8. $\overleftrightarrow{AB}$ and $\overleftrightarrow{CD}$ _____

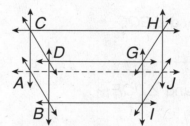

Line $x \parallel$ line y. Find the measure of each.

9. $\angle 1$ and $\angle 6$

10. $\angle 4$ and $\angle 8$

11. $\angle 4$ and $\angle 6$

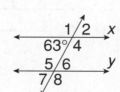

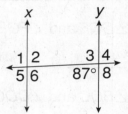

_____   _____   _____

12. $\angle 2$ and $\angle 4$

13. $\angle 5$ and $\angle 7$

14. $\angle 7$ and $\angle 8$

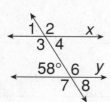

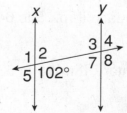

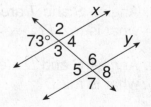

_____   _____   _____

Holt Mathematics

LESSON 8-4 Practice
Properties of Circles

Name the parts of circle A.

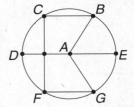

1. radii _____

2. diameters _____

3. chords _____

Name the parts of circle H.

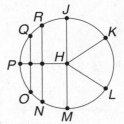

4. radii _____

5. diameters _____

6. chords _____

Name the parts of circle C.

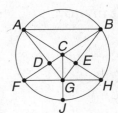

7. radii _____

8. diameters _____

9. chords _____

Name the parts of circle Z.

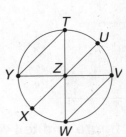

10. radii _____

11. diameters _____

12. chords _____

Use the circle graph.

13. The circle graph shows the distribution of ethnic groups in New Zealand. Find the central angle measure of the sector that shows the percent of New Zealanders who are Maori.

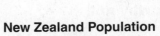

New Zealand Population
Maori 9.7%
Asian/other 7.4%
Other European 4.6%
Pacific Islander 3.8%
New Zealand European 74.5%

_____

Holt Mathematics

Practice
Classifying Polygons

Determine whether each figure is a polygon. If it is not, explain why not.

1.

_____

_____

2.

_____

_____

3.

_____

_____

4.

_____

_____

5.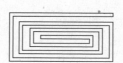

_____

_____

6.

_____

_____

Name each polygon.

7.

_____

8.

_____

9.

_____

10.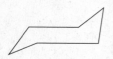

_____

11.

_____

12.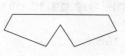

_____

Name each figure and tell whether it is a regular polygon. If it is not, explain why not.

13.

_____

_____

14.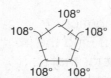

108°
108°   108°
108°   108°

_____

_____

15.
45° 6 ft 45°
6 ft   6 ft
135°   135°
14 ft

_____

_____

Holt Mathematics

Practice

LESSON
8-6 *Classifying Triangles*

Classify each triangle according to its sides and angles.

1.

_____

2.

_____

3.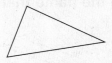

_____

4.

_____

5.

_____

6.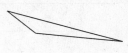

_____

7.

_____

8.

_____

9.

_____

Identify the different types of triangles in each figure and determine how many of each there are.

10.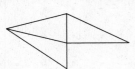

_____ ____

_____

_____

_____

11.

_____ ____

_____

_____

_____

Holt Mathematics

Name _____ Date _____ Class _____

Practice

Classifying Quadrilaterals

Give all of the names that apply to each quadrilateral. Then give the name that best describes it.

1.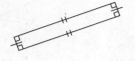

2.

3.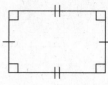

_____

_____

4.

5.

6.

_____

_____

_____

Draw each figure. If it is not possible to draw, explain why.

7. A rectangle that is not a parallelogram.

_____

_____

_____

8. A rectangle that is not a square.

_____

_____

Holt Mathematics

LESSON
8-8
Practice
Angles in Polygons

Find the unknown angle measure in each polygon.

1.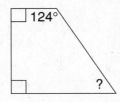

2.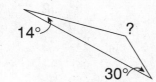

3.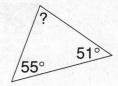

_____

_____

_____

4.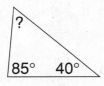

5.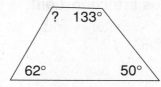

6.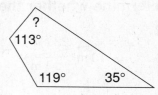

_____

_____

_____

Divide each polygon into triangles to find the sum of its interior angles.

7.

8.

9.

_____

_____

_____

10.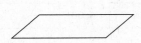

11.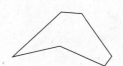

12.

_____

_____

_____

13. A stop sign has the shape of a regular octagon. What is the sum
of the interior angles of a stop sign?

_____

Holt Mathematics

LESSON
8-9
Practice
Congruent Figures

Identify any congruent figures.

1.

_____

_____

2.

_____

_____

Determine whether the triangles are congruent.

3.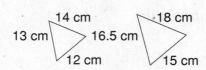

_____

4.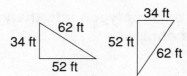

_____

5.

_____

6.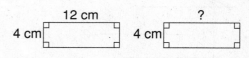

_____

Determine the missing measure or measures in each set of congruent polygons.

7.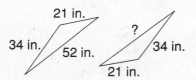

_____

8.   4 cm [12 cm]   4 cm [?]

_____

9.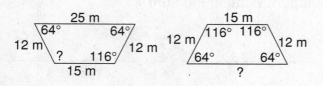

_____

10.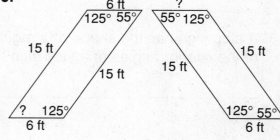

_____

Holt Mathematics

Practice

Translations, Reflections, and Rotations

Identify each type of transformation.

1.

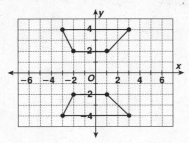

2.

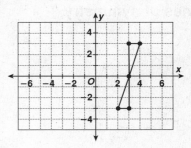

_____

_____

Graph each translation.

3. 5 units to the left and 2 units up

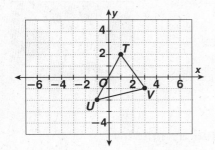

4. 4 units to the right and 3 units up

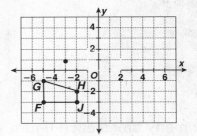

Graph the reflection of each figure across the indicated axis. Write the coordinates of the vertices of the image.

5. *x*-axis

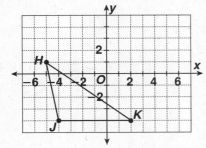

6. *y*-axis

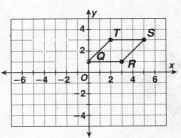

7. Triangle *DEF* has vertices at *D*(−2, −1), *E*(−2, −3), and *F*(−5, −3). Rotate △*DEF* 90° clockwise about the vertex *D*.

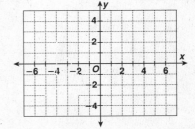

Holt Mathematics

Practice
Symmetry

Decide whether each figure has line symmetry. If it does, draw all the lines of symmetry.

1.

2.

3.

Find and draw all the lines of symmetry in each flag.

4. Iceland

5. Nauru

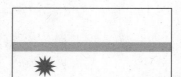

6. Burundi

Tell how many times each figure will show rotational symmetry within one full rotation.

7.

_____

8.

_____

9.

_____

10.

_____

11.

_____

12.

_____

Holt Mathematics

Practice
Accuracy and Precision

Choose the more precise measurement in each pair.

1. 2 tons, 3,700 lb

2. 4 weeks, 27 days

3. 3.5 m, 3.03 m

_____ _____ _____

4. 3 ft, 32 in.

5. 4.6 mL, 2.8 L

6. 15.8 km, 15 km

_____ _____ _____

Determine the number of significant digits in each measurement.

7. 5.801 _____

8. 0.06 _____

9. 75,000 _____

10. 0.00007 _____

11. 100,000,000 _____

12. 300.080 _____

13. 9.007 _____

14. 0.840 _____

15. 0.0050 _____

Calculate. Use the correct number of significant digits in each answer.

16. $21 - 8.6 =$ _____

17. $47.6 + 8 =$ _____

18. $9.8 - 3 =$ _____

19. $31.3 - 24.78 =$ _____

20. $9.63 + 3.4 =$ _____

21. $15.7 + 0.82 =$ _____

22. $0.54 + 0.104 =$ _____

23. $102 - 2.77 =$ _____

24. $62 + 0.319 =$ _____

25. $52.7 \cdot 2.3 =$ _____

26. $8.0 \cdot 1.7 =$ _____

27. $20.5 \div 6.0 =$ _____

28. $23.9 \cdot 14.4 =$ _____

29. $19.2 \div 0.03 =$ _____

30. $1,240 \div 4.025 =$ _____

31. $0.18 \cdot 6.2 =$ _____

32. $95 \div 32 =$ _____

33. $74.3 \cdot 0.22 =$ _____

Holt Mathematics

Name _____ Date _____ Class _____

Practice
Perimeter and Circumference

Find the perimeter of each polygon.

1.
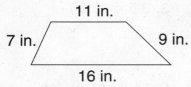
11 in.
7 in.   9 in.
16 in.

_____

2.
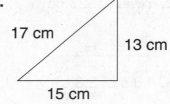
17 cm   13 cm
15 cm

_____

3.
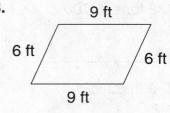
9 ft
6 ft   6 ft
9 ft

_____

Find the perimeter of each rectangle.

4.
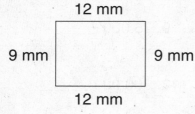
12 mm
9 mm   9 mm
12 mm

_____

5.

3.5 m
10 m   10 m
3.5 m

_____

6.
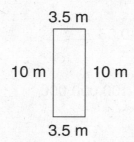
$2\frac{1}{2}$ yd $7\frac{1}{2}$ yd
$7\frac{1}{2}$ yd $2\frac{1}{2}$

_____

Find the circumference of each circle to the nearest tenth.
Use 3.14 for π or $\frac{22}{7}$.

7.

6 in.

_____

8.
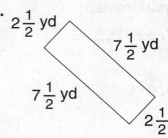
9 cm

_____

9.

1.5 ft

_____

10. A circular swimming pool is 21 feet in diameter. What is the
circumference of the swimming pool? Use $\frac{22}{7}$ for π.   _____

11. A jar lid has a diameter of 42 millimeters. What is the
circumference of the lid? Use $\frac{22}{7}$ for π.   _____

12. A frying pan has a radius of 14 centimeters. What is the
circumference of the frying pan? Use $\frac{22}{7}$ for π.   _____

Holt Mathematics

Practice

LESSON 9-3 *Area of Parallelograms*

Find the area of each rectangle.

1.

13 ft, 8 ft

_____

2.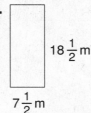

$18\frac{1}{2}$ m, $7\frac{1}{2}$ m

_____

3.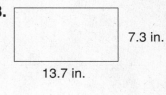

7.3 in., 13.7 in.

_____

Find the area of each parallelogram.

4.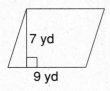

7 yd, 9 yd

_____

5.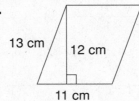

13 cm, 12 cm, 11 cm

_____

6.

5.8 ft, 7.2 ft

_____

7.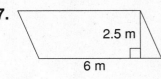

2.5 m, 6 m

_____

8.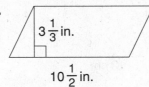

$3\frac{1}{3}$ in., $10\frac{1}{2}$ in.

_____

9.

5.6 m, 2.8 m

_____

10. A dollar bill is 15.5 cm long and 6.5 cm wide. What is the area of a dollar bill?

_____

11. A rectangular hallway has an area of 70 ft². The width of the hallway is 4 feet. What is the length of the hallway?

_____

Holt Mathematics

LESSON 9-4

Practice

Area of Triangles and Trapezoids

Find the area of each triangle.

1.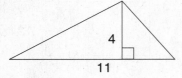

_____

2.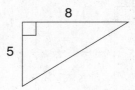

_____

3.

_____

4.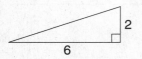

_____

5.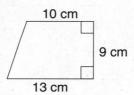

_____

6.

_____

Find the area of each trapezoid.

7.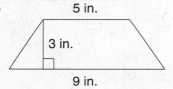

_____

8.

_____

9.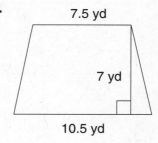

_____

10.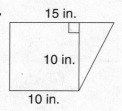

_____

11.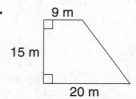

_____

12.

_____

13. The state of Montana is shaped somewhat like a trapezoid. What is the approximate area of Montana?

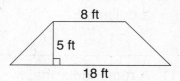

_____

Holt Mathematics

LESSON 9-5

Practice
Area of Circles

Find the area of each circle to the nearest tenth. Use 3.14 for π.

1.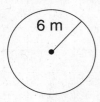
6 m

_____

2.
8 ft

_____

3.
7 yd

_____

4.
5 cm

_____

5.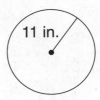
11 in.

_____

6.
3 mm

_____

7.
10 in.

_____

8.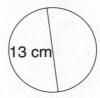
13 cm

_____

9.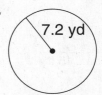
7.2 yd

_____

10. A Susan B. Anthony dollar coin has a diameter of 26.50 millimeters. What is the area of the coin to the nearest hundredth?

_____

11. A tablecloth for a round table has a radius of 21 inches. What is the area of the tablecloth? Use $\frac{22}{7}$ for π.

_____

12. Use a centimeter ruler to measure the radius of the circle. Then find the area of the shaded region of the circle. Use 3.14 for π. Round your answer to the nearest tenth.

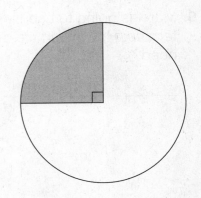

_____

Holt Mathematics

Name _____ Date _____ Class _____

Practice
Area of Irregular Figures

Estimate the area of each figure. Each square represents 1 square foot.

1.
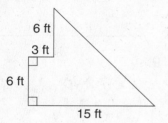

2.
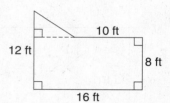

_____   _____

Find the area of each figure. Use 3.14 for π.

3.
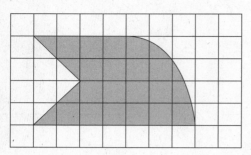

6 ft
3 ft
6 ft
15 ft

4.
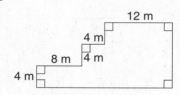

12 m
4 m
8 m
4 m
4 m

5.
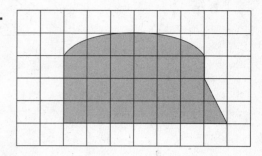

12 ft
10 ft
8 ft
16 ft

_____   _____   _____

6.
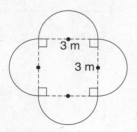

3 m
3 m

7.
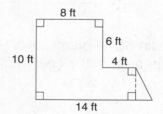

8 ft
6 ft
10 ft
4 ft
14 ft

8.
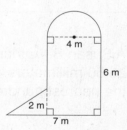

4 m
6 m
2 m
7 m

_____   _____   _____

9. Marci is going to use tile to cover her terrace. How much tile does she need?

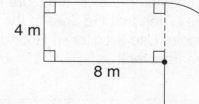

4 m
8 m

_____

Holt Mathematics

LESSON **Practice**
9-7 *Squares and Square Roots*

Find each square.

1. 6^2 _____

2. 19^2 _____

3. 13^2 _____

4. 4^2 _____

5. 10^2 _____

6. 14^2 _____

7. 20^2 _____

8. 18^2 _____

Find each square root.

9. $\sqrt{289}$ _____

10. $\sqrt{49}$ _____

11. $\sqrt{256}$ _____

12. $\sqrt{81}$ _____

13. $\sqrt{121}$ _____

14. $\sqrt{625}$ _____

15. $\sqrt{576}$ _____

16. $\sqrt{900}$ _____

Estimate each square root to the nearest whole number.

17. $\sqrt{11}$ _____

18. $\sqrt{31}$ _____

19. $\sqrt{98}$ _____

20. $\sqrt{50}$ _____

21. $\sqrt{152}$ _____

22. $\sqrt{14}$ _____

23. $\sqrt{70}$ _____

24. $\sqrt{28}$ _____

25. $\sqrt{39}$ _____

26. $\sqrt{193}$ _____

27. $\sqrt{119}$ _____

28. $\sqrt{85}$ _____

29. $\sqrt{5}$ _____

30. $\sqrt{42}$ _____

31. $\sqrt{75}$ _____

32. $\sqrt{215}$ _____

33. The area of a square vegetable garden is 75 ft^2. What is the approximate length of each side of the garden? Find your answer to the nearest foot. _____

34. The area of a square computer screen is 138 in^2. What is the approximate length of each side of the screen? Find your answer to the nearest inch. _____

35. Tim broke a square picture window with his baseball. The area of the window is 52 ft^2. What is the approximate width of the window to be replaced? Find your answer to the nearest foot. _____

36. A square tile has an area of 413 cm^2. What is the approximate length of a side of the tile? Find your answer to the nearest centimeter. _____

Holt Mathematics

LESSON 9-8

Practice
The Pythagorean Theorem

Use the Pythagorean Theorem to find each missing measure.

1.
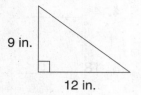

9 in.

12 in.

_____

2.
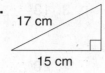

17 cm

15 cm

_____

3.
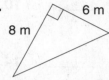

10 ft

24 ft

_____

4.
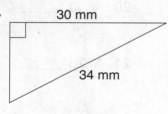

7 m

25 m

_____

5.
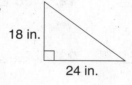

12 yd

13 yd

_____

6.
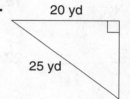

8 m

6 m

_____

7.

30 mm

34 mm

_____

8.

18 in.

24 in.

_____

9.

20 yd

25 yd

_____

10. A 20-ft ladder is leaning against a wall. If the ladder is 12 ft from the base of the wall, how high above the ground does the ladder touch the wall?

_____

11. A checkerboard is 10 inches long on each side. What is the length of the diagonal from one corner to another? Round your answer to the nearest tenth.

_____

12. Chang lives 8 miles east of the school. Deborah lives 12 miles south of the school. Approximately how far apart are Chang's and Deborah's homes? Round your answer to the nearest tenth.

_____

13. A rectangle is 26 meters long and 18 meters wide. What is the length of the diagonal of the rectangle to the nearest meter?

_____

Holt Mathematics

Practice
LESSON 10-1 *Introduction to Three-Dimensional Figures*

Identify the base or bases of each figure. Then name the figure.

1.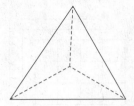

_____

_____

2.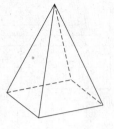

_____

_____

3.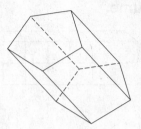

_____

_____

4.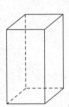

_____

_____

5.

_____

_____

6.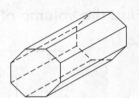

_____

_____

Classify each figure as a polyhedron or not a polyhedron. Then name the figure.

7.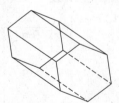

_____

_____

8.

_____

_____

9.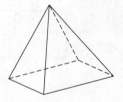

_____

_____

10.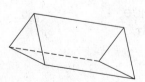

_____

_____

11.

_____

_____

12.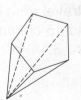

_____

_____

Holt Mathematics

LESSON
10-2

Practice

Volume of Prisms and Cylinders

Find how many cubes each prism holds. Then give the prism's volume.

1.

2.

3.

_____   _____   _____

_____   _____   _____

Find the volume of each figure.

4.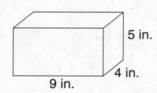
5 in. 4 in. 9 in.

5.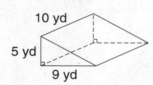
10 yd 5 yd 9 yd

6.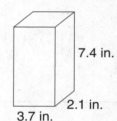
7.4 in. 2.1 in. 3.7 in.

_____   _____   _____

7.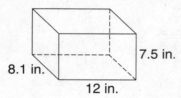
7.5 in. 8.1 in. 12 in.

8.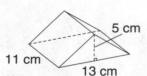
5 cm 11 cm 13 cm

9.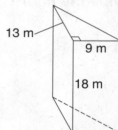
13 m 9 m 18 m

_____   _____   _____

10. A travel mug is shaped like a cylinder. It is 9 centimeters wide and 15 centimeters tall. Find its volume to the nearest tenth. Use 3.14 for π.

_____

Holt Mathematics

Name _____ Date _____ Class _____

Practice

Volume of Pyramids and Cones

Find the volume of each pyramid to the nearest tenth.

1.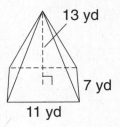
13 yd
7 yd
11 yd

_____

2.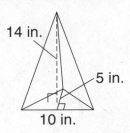
14 in.
5 in.
10 in.

_____

3.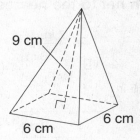
9 cm
6 cm 6 cm

_____

4.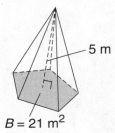
5 m
$B = 21\ m^2$

_____

5.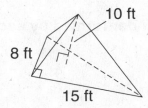
10 ft
8 ft
15 ft

_____

6.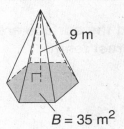
9 m
$B = 35\ m^2$

_____

Find the volume of each cone to the nearest tenth.

7.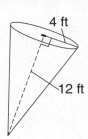
4 ft
12 ft

_____

8.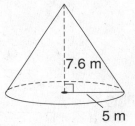
7.6 m
5 m

_____

9.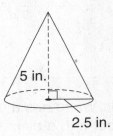
5 in.
2.5 in.

_____

10.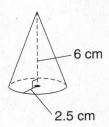
6 cm
2.5 cm

_____

11.
9.8 ft
3 ft

_____

12.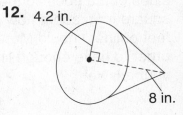
4.2 in.
8 in.

_____

Holt Mathematics

LESSON **Practice**

10-4 *Surface Area of Prisms and Cylinders*

Find the surface area of the prism formed by each net to the nearest tenth.

1.

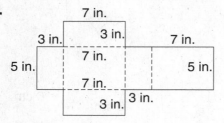

2.

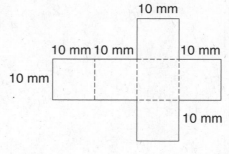

_____   _____

Find the surface area of the cylinder formed by each net to the nearest tenth.

3.

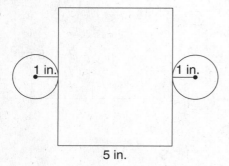

4.

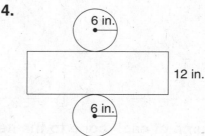

_____   _____

5. Mr. Wang has a circular swimming pool with a diameter of 15 feet and a height of 5 feet. Mr. Wang buys a liner to cover the bottom and the sides of the pool. To the nearest square foot, about how many square feet of liner should Mr. Wang buy in order to have enough liner? Explain your answer.

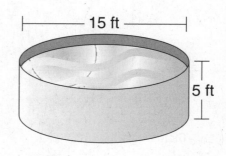

_____

_____

_____

Holt Mathematics

LESSON **Practice**
10-5 *Changing Dimensions*

Given the scale factor, find the surface area of the similar prism.

1. The scale factor of two similar rectangular prisms is 3.
   The surface area of the smaller prism is 15 in^2.   _____

2. The scale factor of two similar triangular prisms is 2.
   The surface area of the smaller prism is 25 cm^2.   _____

3. The scale factor of two similar rectangular prisms is $\frac{1}{2}$.
   The surface area of the larger prism is 960 ft^2.   _____

4. The scale factor of two similar triangular prisms is 5.
   The surface area of the smaller prism is 10 m^2.   _____

5. The scale factor of two similar rectangular prisms is $\frac{1}{5}$.
   The surface area of the larger prism is 625 in^2.   _____

6. The scale factor of two similar pentagonal prisms is 4.
   The surface area of the smaller prism is 16 cm^2.   _____

Given the scale factor, find the volume of the similar prism.

7. The scale factor of two similar triangular prisms is 3.
   The volume of the smaller prism is 8 in^3.   _____

8. The scale factor of two similar rectangular prisms is $\frac{1}{2}$.
   The volume of the larger prism is 648 m^3.   _____

9. The scale factor of two similar triangular prisms is 4.
   The volume of the smaller prism is 10 cm^3.   _____

10. The scale factor of two similar rectangular prisms is $\frac{1}{4}$.
    The volume of the larger prism is 1,920 ft^3.   _____

11. The scale factor of two similar triangular prisms is 2.
    The volume of the smaller prism is 72 yd^3.   _____

12. A small tank weighs 24 pounds when it is full of water.
    A larger tank that is similar in shape has a scale factor
    of 3. How much does the larger tank weigh when filled
    with water?   _____

Holt Mathematics

LESSON	**Practice**
11-1	*Probability*

Determine whether each event is impossible, unlikely, as likely as not, likely, or certain.

1. rolling an even number on a number cube labeled 1 through 6

   _____

2. picking a card with a vowel on it from a box of cards in which each letter of the alphabet is written on a card

   _____

3. spinning a number greater than 2 on a spinner with 10 equal sections marked 1 through 10

   _____

4. drawing a red marble from a bag of black, blue, and green marbles

   _____

5. flipping a coin and getting heads or tails

   _____

6. rolling a number that is less than three 5 times in a row on number on a number cube labeled 1 through 6

   _____

Solve.

7. A bag contains 3 green marbles, 7 blue marbles, and 2 black marbles. The probability of randomly picking a green marble is $\frac{1}{4}$. What is the probability of not picking a green marble?

   _____

8. A spinner has 8 equal sections labeled 1 through 8. The probability of spinning a number that is greater than or equal to 6 is $\frac{3}{8}$. What is the probability of spinning a number that is not greater than or equal to 6?

   _____

9. The probability of randomly drawing a red card from a bag that contains red, blue, and green cards is $\frac{3}{10}$. What is the probability of not drawing a red card?

   _____

10. Myra almost always spends at least 45 minutes on the treadmill. If Myra got on the treadmill at 5:20 P.M., estimate the probability that she will still be on the treadmill at 6:00.

    _____

11. Morris rarely arrives home before 4:00 P.M. It is now 3:20 P.M. Estimate the probability that Morris will arrive home in the next 30 minutes.

    _____

Holt Mathematics

LESSON **Practice**
11-2 *Experimental Probability*

Find the experimental probability. Write your answer as a fraction, as a decimal, and as percent.

1. Jaclyn is a soccer goalie. If she has 21 out of 25 saves in practice, what is the experimental probability that she will have a save on the next shot on goal?   _____

2. If Harris hit the bull's-eye 3 out of 8 times at archery practice, what is the experimental probability that he will hit the bull's-eye on his next try?   _____

3. Nathan inspects new pants at a factory. Of the first 56 pairs of pants he inspected 49 were acceptable. What is the experimental probability that the next pair of pants will be acceptable?   _____

4. Sara has gone to work for 60 days. On 39 of those days she arrived at work before 8:30 A.M. On the rest of the days she arrived after 8:30 A.M. What is the experimental probability that she will arrive at work after 8:30 A.M. the next day she goes to work?   _____

Solve:

5. After a movie premiere, 99 of the first 130 people surveyed said they liked the movie.

   a. What is the experimental probability that the next person surveyed will say he or she liked the movie?   _____

   b. What is the experimental probability that the next person surveyed will say he or she did not like the movie?   _____

6. For the past 30 days, Naomi has been recording the number of customers at her restaurant between 10 A.M. and 11 A.M. During that hour, there have been fewer than 20 customers on 25 out of 30 days.

   a. What is the experimental probability that there will be fewer than 20 customers on the thirty-first day?   _____

   b. What is the experimental probability that there will be more than 20 customers on the thirty-first day?   _____

7. For the past four weeks, Nestor has been recording the daily high temperatures. During that time, the high temperature has been below 45° on 20 out of 28 days. What is the experimental probability that the high temperature will be below 45° on the twenty-ninth day?   _____

Holt Mathematics

LESSON	**Practice**
11-3	***Make a List to Find Sample Spaces***

1. Marcus spins the spinner at the right and flips a dime at the same time. What are the possible outcomes? How many outcomes are in the sample space?

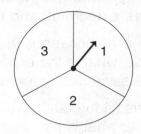

_____

_____

2. For lunch, Britney has a choice of a hot dog, a hamburger, or pizza and a choice of an apple, a pear, or grapes. What are all the possible choices of lunch she can have? How many outcomes are in the sample space?

_____

_____

_____

_____

3. Susan and Ryan are playing a game that involves spinning the spinner at the right and flipping a penny. How many outcomes are possible in the game?

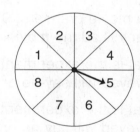

_____

4. An Italian restaurant offers small, medium, and large calzones. The choices of fillings are cheese, sausage, spinach, or vegetable. How many different calzones can you order?

_____

5. There are 5 ways to go from Town X to Town Y. There are 3 ways to go from Town Y to Town Z. How many different ways are there to go from Town X to Town Z, passing through Town Y?

_____

6. Rasheed has tan pants, black pants, gray pants, and blue pants. He has a brown sweater and a white sweater. How many different ways can he wear a sweater and pants together?

_____

Holt Mathematics

LESSON 11-4 **Practice**
Theoretical Probability

Find the probability of each event. Write your answer as a fraction, as a decimal, and as a percent. Round to the nearest tenth of a percent.

1. randomly choosing a white counter from a bag of 12 red counters, 12 white counters, 12 green counters, and 12 blue counters

   _____

2. tossing two fair coins and having one land on tails and one land on heads

   _____

3. rolling a number greater than 1 on a fair number cube

   _____

4. randomly drawing an orange disk from a bag of 14 black disks, 4 blue disks and 12 orange disks

   _____

5. randomly drawing 1 of the 6 R's from a bag of 100 Scrabble tiles

   _____

6. spinning a number less than 7 on a fair spinner with 8 equal sections labeled 1-8

   _____

A set of cards has 20 cards with stars, 10 cards with squares, and 15 cards with circles. Find the probability of each event when a card is chosen at random.

7. square _____   8. circle _____

9. star or circle _____   10. not circle or square _____

There are 14 girls and 18 boys in Ms. Wiley's class. Ms. Wiley randomly selects one student to solve a problem. Find the probability of each event.

11. selecting a boy _____   12. selecting a girl _____

Holt Mathematics

LESSON 11-5 Practice

Probability of Independent and Dependent Events

Decide if each set of events is independent or dependent. Explain your answer.

1. A student spins a spinner and chooses a Scrabble® tile

_____

_____

2. A boy chooses a sock from a drawer of socks, then chooses a second sock without replacing the first.

_____

_____

3. A student picks a raffle ticket from a box, replaces the ticket, then picks a second raffle ticket.

_____

_____

Find the probability of each set of independent events.

4. drawing a red checker from a bag of 9 black checkers and 6 red checkers, replacing it, and drawing another red checker

_____

5. drawing a black checker from a bag of 9 black checkers and 6 red checkers, replacing it, and drawing a red checker

_____

6. rolling a 1, 2, or 3 on the first roll of a 1–6 number cube and rolling a 4, 5, or 6 on the second roll of the same cube

_____

Solve.

7. Randy has 4 pennies, 2 nickels, and 3 dimes in his pocket. If he randomly chooses 2 coins, what is the probability that both are dimes?

_____

Holt Mathematics

Practice
Combinations

1. A chef has some broccoli, cauliflower, carrots, and squash to make a vegetarian dish. List the possible combinations if he uses only 3 vegetables in the dish.

_____

_____

_____

2. Lauren, Manuel, Nick, Opal, and Pat are forming groups of two to work on a drama production. List the different combinations of students that are possible using the first initial of each name.

_____

3. Keiko has seven colors of lanyard. She uses three different colors to make a key chain. How many different combinations can she choose?

_____

4. On Sundays at Ice Cream Heaven, you can choose two free toppings for your sundae. The toppings are nuts, hot fudge, caramel, and sprinkles. How many different combinations of toppings can you order?

_____

5. How many different three-person relay teams can be chosen from six students?

_____

6. The students in Mrs. Mandel's class need to choose two class representatives from six nominated students. How many different combinations of class representatives are possible?

_____

7. There are four varieties of muffins available at the Coffee Shop. How many different ways can you choose three different muffins?

_____

8. How many two-person carpools are possible with seven people?

_____

Holt Mathematics

Practice
Permutations

1. Joe has homework assignments for math, Spanish, and history. In how many different orders can he do his homework?

_____

2. Find the number of permutations of the letters in the word SMART.

_____

3. In how many ways can you arrange the numbers 6, 7, 8, and 9 to make a four-digit number?

_____

4. A table has 8 seats. In how many different ways can 8 people sit at the table?

_____

5. Nine mountain bikers are on a bicycle trip. In how many possible ways can they follow each other?

_____

6. Seven students are waiting in line at the cafeteria. In how many different orders can they be standing in line?

_____

7. How many permutations of the letters A through F are there?

_____

8. Ed, Martine, Sal, Carl, Paula, Terry, Ken, Leo, Ursula, and Jamie are in a race. In how many different orders can they finish?

_____

9. Find the number of permutations of the letters in the word *permutations.*

_____

10. In how many different orders can 11 people stand in line?

_____

11. In how many different ways can a librarian arrange eight books on a shelf?

_____

12. Melinda has 15 art trophies. Write an expression that shows how many different ways she can line up her trophies on a shelf.

_____

Holt Mathematics

Solve. Check each answer.

1. $7x + 8 = 36$

2. $-3y - 7 = 2$

3. $4a - 13 = 19$

_____

_____

_____

4. $6a - 4 = -2$

5. $5k + 2 = 6$

6. $9m - 14 = -8$

_____

_____

_____

Solve.

7. $\frac{v}{4} - 3 = 5$

8. $\frac{u}{5} + 3 = 1$

9. $6 + \frac{z}{9} = 9$

_____

_____

_____

10. $-7 + \frac{f}{2} = -1$

11. $9 + \frac{w}{4} = -5$

12. $\frac{e}{7} - 3 = -5$

_____

_____

_____

13. $-8 + \frac{d}{5} = 2$

14. $\frac{u}{5} + 3 = 6$

15. $\frac{f}{-3} + 5 = 8$

_____

_____

_____

16. Two years of local Internet service costs $685, including the installation fee of $85. What is the monthly fee?

_____

Holt Mathematics

Solve.

1. $15x - 8 - 3x = 16$ **2.** $5n + 3 + 4n = 30$ **3.** $h - 6 + 7h = 42$

_____   _____   _____

4. $-3g + 6 + 2g = 15$ **5.** $-2b + 7 - 3b = 2$ **6.** $5y + 1 + 3y = -15$

_____   _____   _____

7. $4k - 14 + 3k = 21$ **8.** $9m + 10 - 14m = -5$ **9.** $-2d + 18 - 4d = 60$

_____   _____   _____

10. $3(n + 5) + 2 = 26$ **11.** $4 - 2(v - 6) = -8$ **12.** $1.4 - 1.6(t + 6) = 4.6$

_____   _____   _____

13. $2.4(m - 3) + 3.8 = -8.2$ **14.** $6 = 8(s - \frac{3}{4}) - 20$ **15.** $5(c + \frac{4}{5}) + 6 = 50$

_____   _____   _____

16. Joel has twice as many CDs as Mariella has. Subtracting 7 from
the number of CDs Joel has and dividing by 3 equals the
number of CDs Blake has. If Blake has 25 CDs, how many CDs
does Mariella have?

_____

         Holt Mathematics

LESSON 12-3

Practice

Solving Equations with Variables on Both Sides

Group the terms with the variables on one side of the equal sign and simplify.

1. $10t = 6t + 24$

2. $-6x - 32 = 2x$

3. $j = 20 - 4j$

4. $-5d + 40 = 5d$

5. $9m - 28 = 2m$

6. $\frac{8}{9}x = 8 + \frac{4}{9}x$

Solve.

7. $8k = 6k - 26$

8. $32 - 5v = 3v + 8$

9. $-12y - 10 = -6y + 14$

10. $\frac{5}{8}a + 6 = \frac{3}{4}a$

11. $\frac{1}{4}n + 10 = \frac{2}{3}n$

12. $20 - \frac{1}{5}d = \frac{3}{10}d + 16$

13. Members of the Lake Shawnee Club pay $40 per summer season plus $7.50 each time they rent a boat. Nonmembers pay $12.50 each time they rent a boat. How many times would both a member and a nonmember have to rent a boat in order to pay the same amount? _____

Holt Mathematics

Practice
LESSON
12-4 *Inequalities*

Write an inequality for each situation.

1. The temperature today will be at most 50°F. _____

2. The temperature tomorrow will be above 70°F. _____

3. Yesterday, there was less than 2 inches of rain. _____

4. Last Monday, there was at least 3 inches of rain. _____

Graph each inequality.

5. $t \leq -2$

6. $j > -5$

7. $y \leq 0$

8. $b < \frac{1}{2}$

Graph each compound inequality.

9. $f > 3$ or $f < -2$

10. $-4 \leq w \leq 4$

11. $b < 0$ or $b \geq 5$

12. $y \geq 3$ or $y \leq -1$

13. $-4 < m < -2$

Holt Mathematics

Name _____ Date _____ Class _____

Solve. Then graph each solution set on a number line.

1. $y - 5 > -2$ _____

2. $n + 5 \leq 11$ _____

3. $x + 4 < -1$ _____

4. $h + 20 > 2$ _____

5. $p + 9 \geq -3$ _____

6. $s - 7 < -16$ _____

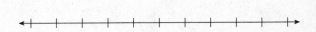

Solve. Check each answer.

7. $41 + g > 27$

8. $w + 23 \geq -18$

9. $a + 15 \leq 9$

_____

10. $z + 27 < 16$

_____

11. $-3 \leq t + 17$

_____

12. $78 \geq b + 64$

_____

_____

_____

13. In order for a field trip to be scheduled, at least 30 students must sign up. So far, 23 students have signed up. At least how many more students must sign up in order for the field trip to be scheduled?

_____

Holt Mathematics

LESSON 12-6 Practice

Solving Inequalities by Multiplying or Dividing

Solve.

1. $\dfrac{n}{5} \le 1.6$

2. $\dfrac{b}{3} > -8$

3. $\dfrac{a}{3} \ge -9$

_____   _____   _____

4. $\dfrac{t}{-6} < -7$

5. $\dfrac{s}{-12} \le -5$

6. $\dfrac{r}{5.3} \le 6$

_____   _____   _____

Solve. Check each answer.

7. $8c < -64$

8. $-16a \ge -24$

9. $-12t > 9$

_____   _____   _____

10. $-3s \le -180$

11. $18b > -24$

12. $-6m \ge 4$

_____   _____   _____

13. It cost Sophia $530 to make wind chimes. How many wind chimes must she sell at $12 apiece to make a profit?

_____

14. It cost the Wilson children $55 to make lemonade. How many glasses must they sell at 75¢ each to make a profit?

_____

15. Jorge's soccer team is having its annual fund raiser. The team hopes to earn at least three times as much as it did last year. Last year the team earned $87. What is the team's goal for this year?

_____

Holt Mathematics

Practice
LESSON 12-7 Solving Two-Step Inequalities

Solve. Then graph each solution set on a number line.

1. $5x - 8 < 17$ _____

2. $\dfrac{r}{3} + 5 \geq 9$ _____

3. $-4n + 8 < -4$ _____

4. $\dfrac{z}{7} - 6 \geq -5$ _____

5. $\dfrac{w}{-5} + 4 < 9$ _____

6. $\dfrac{u}{2} - 5 \leq -9$ _____

Solve.

7. $-7d + 8 > 29$

8. $4g - 18 \leq -2$

9. $12 - 3b < 9$

_____

_____

_____

10. $\dfrac{a}{-4} - 7 < -2$

11. $9 + \dfrac{c}{6} \leq 17$

12. $-\dfrac{2}{3}p - 8 \geq 4$

_____

_____

13. Fifty students in the seventh grade are trying to raise at least $2,000 for sports supplies. They have already raised $750. How much should each student raise, on average, in order to meet the goal?

_____

Holt Mathematics